W9-DIY-503

# MARY'S MESSAGE

## The Alternative Story of Mary Magdalene & Jesus

## Ann Crawford

© 2018 by Lightscapes Publishing

Previous versions published 2008 and 2013

All rights reserved. This book or any portion thereof may not be reproduced or used in any manner whatsoever without the express written permission of the publisher.

For permission to quote brief passages, please contact: info@lightscapespublishing.com.

Printed in the United States of America

First Printing, 2008

ISBN-13: 978-1-948543-22-4 (paperback)
ISBN-13: 978-1-948543-23-1 (eBook)

Distributed by Bublish, Inc.
Cover Art by Geoffrey Benzing

www.anncrawford.net

*For*
*Steve*

This is a work of fiction and is not based on the Gospels or any historical text.

Quotes from the bible are in italics and are from the King James Version. The verses used are referenced at the end of the book.

I came so that you may *have life,*
*and...have it more abundantly.*

Jesus of Nazareth,
called herein by his Aramaic name
Yeshua ben Yosef


I came so that you may
remember who you really are.

Mary of Magdala

# A MESSAGE

Oh, beautiful, beautiful Life on Earth. You are meant to be a celebration—one lifelong, living, breathing, moving, continuous, everlasting celebration. You are meant to be a delightful feast of the heart, mind, soul, and spirit.

At least that was the design.

But a long time ago, the primary event of the day was staying alive. We did not understand living and dying, sickness and deformity, weather patterns and natural disasters, the odd series of seemingly random unfortunate events, even life itself...so, in order to gain some semblance of understanding of the strange happenings of life, we made things up. We made up gods to explain the fickle forces of nature and the cosmos, along with the apparent irrational distribution of illness and hardship, and then we appeased the gods we made up with prayers and sacrifices, which we also made up. If sacrificing an animal seemed to appease the gods of rain, well then perhaps sacrificing an infant would appease them even more. It certainly sounds insane in the present day, but how many things are made up and done now that will seem just as insane in another five or ten thousand years?

We learned to suppress people, for reasons we made up. We learned to suppress our spirit and our natural urges, for reasons we made up. The family where the husband and wife were committed and faithful to each other was the family that survived, so straying eventually became an error punishable by banishment or worse. Yes, commitment and fidelity are wonderful— but they should be developed and followed in the heart for their own sake, not to avoid external punishment by made-up legislation from some self-elected, made-up group of legislators.

We found that when we restricted many activities and hid ourselves away in tight-knit groups, we could concentrate on that very important job at hand, that of staying alive and ensuring the survival of our children. And the tribe that banded together had a greater chance of survival, so marrying beyond the tribe became unmentionable. Even sharing love and acceptance for those outside the tribe became unforgivable. Certain foods or foods eaten in certain combinations that had occasional fatal repercussions were outlawed. We created rules and regulations—No, you cannot marry that person! Do not eat that! You cannot think that way!—that sometimes lived far longer than the human foibles, dilemmas, and experiences they were to protect. The safety and security of the entire tribe was at risk—people watched their loved ones die when these regulations were not followed—so who could blame our ancestors and ourselves in our earlier forms for putting together these kinds of made-up things into societal conventions?

Since the outside world grabbed hold of our attention so fiercely that most people did not even consider delving into the inside world, our appetite for all things external grew. We did not understand the sacredness of our very lives, and we learned to kill anything or anyone that stood in the way of what we wanted—food, land, expansion, domination. As we fed ourselves more, more, more, our appetites grew and we wanted more, more, more—just to have more, more, more.

We were frightened...and, although we were doing our best, it was clearly not the best we could do.

Oh, beloved Life on Earth. Somehow, some way, the

celebration got extinguished. You are supposed to be a banquet for all of the senses, a kaleidoscope of experiences and adventures, an expansion of the heart, an opening to infinity. How did we get it so wrong? So many people were confused and then someone, also scared and threatened, inadvisably had some power to wield. Just imagine the absurdity of creating a world where part or even up to half the population was subservient to the other. Even today slavery still exists. Even today to see a woman's face—let alone other parts of her incredibly beautiful body—is still outlawed in some sectors. Imagine so suppressing the natural spark in men to create life leading to the suppression of women...oh! Clearly the glory that is life was not understood. Imagine the pain someone must have been enduring to create policies proclaiming fun as a sin. Dancing, singing, laughing, intimacy—a sin, of all things! Unfortunately, we do not have to imagine the absurdity of it; we still live with the results of some mad imaginings from long ago and there are places, even now, where these are outlawed in many forms. Self-hatred comes from not understanding our true design, and cruelty is our own self-hatred transferred into action.

Life is also supposed to be easier than we seem to be making it. But really the only thing that makes it hard is our own resistances that arise for whatever reason, whether it is training or habit or karma or soul choices or pre-incarnation soul agreements or some combination of all of these. We all decide what we are going to work on in each life. In that regard there are no victims, ever. And, when there are no victims, the power is in our hands.

Plus, we are coming to know better now. Life is about joy. Life is about love. Life is about light and laughter, growth and expansion, giving and receiving, dancing and playing, singing and silliness, depth of understanding and broader scopes of vision, and education and evolution of our beings, giving birth, and, yes, even dying to an outmoded body vessel or way of being, and rebirthing ourselves...over and over and over and over again.

Yes, there are times of pain and sorrow, but they really only serve to strengthen and fortify us for the long run. We face loneliness, hardship, wars, torture, worse. I keep saying worse, but there is nothing that is really bad, other than the temporary suffering of the heart when someone we love dies or our work efforts fail or something similar, but we recover from that.

We do not really die anyway. Not one thing is ever created or destroyed, thus we were never born so we cannot die. We only transform. We've always been; then we come here for a while, and when our time is done we just lay this body down and pick up something else somewhere else. Here, hereafter, there, before, during, after, anywhere, everywhere—yes, it's all one lifelong, living, breathing, moving, continuous, everlasting miracle.

What would you do if I told you that a lot of what you have been taught was wrong? At this point many of us have more to unlearn than to learn. We have millennia of fear coursing through our veins, inherited from our scared, fearful ancestors and our earlier selves who were doing their best to preserve their own lives and to make it possible for us to be here at all. They did a wonderful job in many ways. But most of them knew so very little about their true nature and the reality of life in our universe.

It is time to know that you hold more power in the palm of your hand than is in the mighty winds, or than is in the power of the large vehicles that race across the planet or hurtle through space now, or than is in entire cities, countries, continents. If you were not here, something extremely important—something vital and essential—would be missing from the divine tapestry that is the whole of creation.

But you are here, thank God/Goddess/All That Is. You always were and you always will be. And the time of deep slumber is over.

Wake up!

☼

Yeshua ben Yosef lived among us two thousand years ago. You know the story, at least some of it. His counterpart, his partner in his life's mission, also lived two thousand years ago, but you do not hear very much about her. The retelling of a story is often more about the reteller than the subject itself. And who did most of the retelling? There were also many things that were told that are absolutely not true, as the telling was part of an agenda of a particular age...and to give the crazy notions more power, they were attributed to something that had all power: God. You really cannot argue with the only Son of God, now, can you?

Some of the things that we do not have to unlearn are the things he taught: love thy neighbor; pray, believing it is so, and you will have whatever you want; the greatest of all qualities is love; bless those that try to hurt you; the domain of Heaven is within; along with the many, many other great teachings attributed to him, our great Teacher. Those are true. And so are the things he taught that were not written down properly: there is more than enough...of everything. Everyone's going to Heaven...because we are already in Heaven, to the extent that we are aware and open to it. War is not part of a civilized society, nor is suppression of any kind. He emphasized that when you pray, believing, and obtain whatever it is that you want, make sure that it is serving the higher good of you and all and harms no one. It is so interesting how one strand of a particular famous teaching was deleted, over and over... although some chronicles of words attributed to him were downright wrong: There is not to be poor always—he never said that! Does that seem to be something a compassionate person would say? So-called good Christians spout that line, thinking they are quoting God, but I think it came about the way it did as an excuse to be lazy and complacent—after all, working toward the betterment and equality of all of society requires a great deal of ingenuity and hard work. And true equality for all remains frightening to some. But when we know who we truly are, nothing can truly frighten us any more.

A great many things our great Teacher told us remain idle, taken out of context, misconstrued, or even used as a justification for unspeakable acts. And a few things were kept secret, until now.

I want to show you another side of the story you have heard so many times.

Come, walk with me.

# CHAPTER 1

Only the knowledge that there was another life inside of me kept me on this side of the veil, somewhat. Other-wise there was only the pain, only the searing pain...and without the sense of the life stirring within, for a moment I might have disappeared into the flames of the anguish, never to return.

I reached the shelter and shadows of the tall rocks. My knees gave out under me and I sank into the sand, grateful for the cool against my burning flesh. I shivered despite the heat of the morning sun, trying to catch my breath. My fingers reached out to the rock next to me. At first I could barely sense its rough hardness, but then my hand pressed against it, as if I could somehow transmit my pain into the stone, and as if somehow the cold hardness could bear some of the grief for me. It worked for a moment, but then the grief seared my heart again. I was beyond tears. Tears were for before, when it was bad enough. I had no idea it could become worse.

The pain was everywhere: in my breath, in my blood, in my tears. There was only the pain, except for the rock, which reminded me that there was something in the world other than the pain that engulfed me...and except also for the miracle of life stirring within my womb—a distant reminder from the center of my being that life loves to re-create itself, despite many seeming obstacles thrown in its path.

It was one thing if there had been a tremendous injustice that could take my beloved from me, and I would never see him again in this lifetime. It was one thing if my beautiful partner, my twin spirit, my counterpart, was taken from me and just killed. I had

had more than enough people die in my life to know that often they do not really go anywhere—that the relationship can continue when one is in the flesh and the other is not. Yes, that was all one thing, and it might have been much, much easier.

But life is not always meant to be the easier path.

So I let the anguish devour me in the shadows of the rocks, for just a while longer.

☼

The sun sank lower in the horizon. I did not know how long I had been there, clutching the rock, but I did know they were waiting for me. I held my stomach as I struggled to my feet. I wavered for a moment and then slipped to the sand again. If this new life inside me could survive the grief its mother was enduring, it could survive just about anything.

I heard him then, calling to me, speaking my name, reminding me about the bigger view, the higher purpose. I rose to my feet again.

☼

Yes, I knew what the big view was. I knew that there was a higher calling for things, despite appearances. But I also knew that while the anguish was so all-encompassing, all-consuming, there was nothing else to do but let it have its way with me until it passed. And then when it comes back, to let it have its way again until it passes again. That is how we heal. If we push away the feelings and emotions of the great tragedies that come to us, they will eventually consume us one way or another, and most likely in a way not to our liking—perhaps sickness, perhaps misfortune.

The strength required to do this sometimes seems

like it is more than human. It _is_ more than human. But then so are we. We are amazing beings of love and bone and light and sinew and spirit and matter and eternity and flesh. We are where Heaven and Earth meet...and sometimes the meeting is smooth, and sometimes it is a harrowing storm. It is our job to keep our ship sailing as best as possible, even through rough waters.

We do not know the full reason behind anything, really. How did we get here? Why would a baby die just weeks after its birth? Why would an otherwise just ruler sentence an innocent person to death? Why would someone suffer the murder of her child? Why would a relentless rain destroy a season's crops right before harvest? Why anything? Is it karma? Fate? A capricious, angry God? Or maybe it was a plan made long before we descended into our body—a plan we devised to further our soul's evolution?

No matter what the cause, we are all responsible for our response to our experience on Earth, possibly in addition to the experience itself, and so I could only do what I could do, knowing that truth. I picked myself up, straightened my back and squared my shoulders, and left the sands to join the others who had been waiting for me—remembering that my beloved and I created this for his and my own evolution...and that of everyone else who has been alive in the past two thousand years and everyone who will come in the future.

# CHAPTER 2

My name is Mary. I come from Magdala.

Well, actually, I come from a lot more than Magdala, but the time I walked on Earth, the time you have heard about, I was born in Magdala. I come from a much greater place than that, however, and so do you. You may know me as many different things but, as I told you earlier, the way things are retold and remembered often have much more to do with the ones who are doing the retelling than the actual person they are telling about.

In the time I walked the Earth with Yeshua, I was a healer. A priestess. A wisdomkeeper. Surprised? Oh, do not be. Has anyone ever said anything about you that is very different from who you really are—yesterday? It can become worse as thousands of years pass, I can assure you, if that is part of a set agenda.

He and I came just that one time, as us. But we came infinite times, in infinite places, as we all do, as part of the whole design. And the most interesting thing is that almost anyone could have done what we did or taught what we taught. We were just like you...only, perhaps, a little more so.

More about what I mean by that later.

As I mentioned, you know some of the story of what happened. But what you do know, you know from the point of view of who wrote it, and the point of view of their own plans and schemes. In the stories passed down over the years, Yeshua was elevated to God, a status that cannot be obtained by humans. But he was human, although, yes, I just stated that we are all more than human. But he was human in the same way that we all are. His mother was given another impossible, unattainable status: that of a virgin mother. And I was relegated to one of the lowest of levels: a whore. Either direction, they were levels that ordinary humans could not or, in the case of my designation, would not go.

But we were just like you.

There is not one of you who walks on the Earth as me—I do not walk the Earth any more. But there are many of you who walk on Earth with my energy, just as there are many who walk with Yeshua's energy or with Mother Mary's energy. Or with the energy of anyone and everyone else, ever, in the eternal course of time. We carry whomever we choose.

It does not matter if you are an old soul or if this is your first time on this journey on this particular planet. You are really a very old entity, part of the whole that was never born and can never die, that will always be here, forever expanding and expressing, just like the very universe itself.

As is each one of us.

☼

Israel was the Promised Land—a land, literally, of so many, many promises. Jerusalem has been a city of converging peoples and thoughts for a very long time. At the time Yeshua and I were there, we were a colony of Rome—a rogue colony, at that. The Romans did not quite know what to do with us. Usually whenever two peoples meet, even when the meeting comes by force, ultimately the lives of both are bettered. They bettered our lives with civil engineering and development of infrastructure, and with such mechanical things as aqueducts, sewer systems, and roads. We bettered theirs with items that we cannot see, hear, taste, smell, touch in the physical world but that enhance the world of the spirit immeasurably: the richness of our faith, the solidity of our one God, the profound love of our one God, and the close unity of our people.

When two armies and two worlds crash, one of the benefits is the planting of the seed of the men in the bodies of the women. Oh, if it were only as poetic as that and not such a devastating tragedy for the women who writhe with agony, crushed on the ground under the weight of not only a man usurping her rights, dignity, and inner sanctity, but also the weight of the war itself, ravaging her body as well as the land. They take from her as they take from the villages. But they leave behind a legacy

So we had people who were forbidden from going outside their tribe, for the protection of the tribe....and we had the furtherance of humanity by the warring armies taking their brides by force and planting their seeds in foreign lands, for the eventual betterment of both races and humanity itself. If we repress a basic, primal urge, we tend to explode somewhere else. Absolutely fascinating—so much evil, and yet so much good. That is a recurring theme on this planet.

Even today there are prejudices and judgments against others, ethnocentric pride, racism, feelings of supremacy, and an urge for domination. We are such a confused, young species, really. We are only a hundred thousand years old, if that, in our present form. Whales are millions of years old, as a comparison. Our star is very young, as stars go. Our planet is very young, as planets go. And we are children, playing those favorite children's games of house, war, school, and other facets of grownup living. Well, so-called grownup living at any rate.

But Yeshua and I lived in the land of milk and honey, the land of so many promises. The homeland of our people. We were Jewish by culture, but we did not adhere to the strict religious doctrines of our people. We followed our way of living from the cosmos, much to the distress and consternation of those who lived around us. It certainly made for an interesting life.

It was a time of such scarcity, despite the reputation of milk and honey flowing and flowing and flowing. We were living in a place that had little fresh water at times. Growing crops could be very difficult. Children often died at very early ages. Hearts were sore and frightened and confused. Spirits were suppressed and obedient to the cultural requirements...or they were banished or extinguished.

Fear was rampant. A hostile foreign entity was in charge of the government. The hypocritical publicans ran the religious endeavors. We lived in a part of the world where three continents, three very different ways of living, collided. There was little light shining in anyone's eyes. For most of the populace it was enough to get one's wares to the market to make money to purchase food and goods...so another day of just holding home, hearth, and family together was a good day indeed. Yeshua and I and the group we traveled with were complete unknown anomalies to most of the general public. It was very difficult to live in those upper echelons of existence and then deal with the gross density of the greed, tunnel vision, narrow-mindedness, superstition, and mistrust—all arising from intense fear.

But we certainly count ourselves as among the much, much more fortunate ones of the day, even given everything that happened.

☼

When had I first seen him? It was before he went to

the East the first time, so he was in his late teenage years and I was just a little older, twenty years. Most women were married and had several children by that age, but I had been taken from that path. Shortly after my blossoming, I was taken to a special school, for special girls, for special lessons...I would learn the ways of the High Priestess.

Most women of my time were trained in the activities of running a home: cooking, sewing, cleaning, gardening, and farming. I was trained in the activities of running a home, a palace, a collective farming community, a business enterprise, a temple, and schools of many types.

Most women of my time were taught to rely on men; I was taught to defend myself, to overcome fear, to vanquish desires if the timing warranted such, and to rely entirely and solely on myself. I spent nights alone in dark caves; days in the scorching desert, with no company except a scorpion, whom I quickly learned to befriend; weeks on the open sea fishing; fasting for weeks at a time; journeying by foot for days on end with not one extra article of clothing, food, or bedding...in short, anything and everything the priestesses who came ahead of me thought would teach me that the only person to totally rely on, ever, was myself.

Nearly all women of my time were taught that the activity of a man and woman coupling was a chore, an unavoidable requirement, and not necessarily a pleasant one at that. I was trained that not only was it pleasant, it was one of the greatest gifts of love and pleasure that two beings can give one another. I was trained since my early teens in the lovemaking techniques, and in my later teens I started training young men in the art of love. Of course, in the earlier years it was spoken instruction until the time I was deemed ready enough to experience it fully, without fear or hesitation, but with only an all-encompassing desire for this incredible moment of awakening and opening. And then the men I trained were taught by the best.

Sexuality is one of the most beautiful gifts of life—a sacred, holy, high moment of union. But when people are in fear, they are controllable. When they are told that one of the most natural, beautiful parts of life is something shameful, they become repressed. Repression leads to self-loathing, and those who loathe themselves will do anything for approval, including ill, including hurting themselves, and including hurting others in the name of some made-up ruler, some made-up rules, or in the name of some made-up God to further some made-up ruler's agenda.

Imagine a beautiful rose feeling shame, or a lion hiding himself away, diminishing his drive so much that it has to break out in an uncontrollable fashion from time to time. For that is what society has created. In some cultures, the women are blamed and hence they are covered from head to foot. Absolute insanity! But when a major part of our identity is shunned, turned off, it can only lead to trouble.

The human form is one of the most beautiful creations ever, well, created. The power that brings us together to create life is one of the most powerful forces on Earth. When we consider how extremely strong this force is and how much this power has attempted to be diminished and suppressed from time immemorial, it is actually amazing society has done as well as it has.

Two people coming together in sexual ecstasy is one of the most loving gifts that we have been given and one of the most loving gifts that we can give back to our creator. The trainings I had and gave had absolutely nothing lascivious about them. They were sacred. The teachings took one of our basic human functions and lifted it up to the level of high spirituality and service.

The men I trained were trained in the art of respect, reverence, and generosity of spirit and body...perhaps those old-time notions might be returning here and there, but for the most part, making love is not making love, it is just....

Anyway, I digress. I could go on about sexuality for decades because it has been relegated to the dregs of society for so long, when it really belongs in the higher realms of life.

Back to my training...I was trained in the physical healing arts, using herbs, plants, oils, touch. I was taught to heal with energy, heal with thought and imagery, and heal with my heart, even from far away. I was trained to hear beyond what people told me their symptoms were and to read what their bodies wanted to tell me; I could scan a person, holding my hands just a couple of inches from the body itself, and "see and hear"—with my hands—what the problem was and how it could best be resolved. I heard many a newborn's first cry as I was trained to welcome babies to this side of the veil and to care for their mother, so that the new lives would be given the utmost loving nurturance. I trained many a father to provide the most loving care and nurturance to his family. I also heard many last words as I was trained to bid farewell to souls as they left their bodies to the dust of this realm and to guide them to the loving hands that patiently waited to assist them on the other side of the veil. And I tended to the loved ones they left behind, and I tried to help them see and feel their newly departed ones' joy in their newly discovered world.

And mostly I was trained in the spiritual realms. I was taught about our divine heritage...the true nature of reality and of humanity. I learned that there is no God way out there—we all are, everything is, God/Goddess in form—and to treat everything, everyone, myself included, with the respect due a child of All There Is. I learned to embrace all of creation into me, my meditations, my daily work. I was trained in the power of prayer—not in a manner that is pleading with some unseen entity, but that it is a way to gain clarity and enable the highest purpose of anyone's life to unfold. I was trained in the use of my mind to create days of joy and beauty and a life of power and service. I could speak to others on the airstreams and thought-streams that circle the planet. I could see the shimmering aliveness of a tree or a blade of grass. I could see the light that shines around everyone and knew who was safe to approach and who was not. Voices spoke to me from other dimensions. One thing I had never heard, yet knew that others had experienced, was the music of the spheres. But I learned to follow inner direction; I could discern which internal voice was the one to follow and which would lead me at first to pleasantries but ultimately to regret.

Sometimes when my young students would ask me what I had to teach them, I told them, "I came so that you may remember who you really are." When they asked me if I remembered, I could honestly answer, "Yes."

I never met anyone who could come even close to matching my capabilities, until I met him.

☼

Yeshua. His very name was an affirmation of life. I saw him only briefly before he set off for foreign lands. The temple was celebrating the return of springtime. Numerous strangers thronged to the palace grounds, and he was with a group of young men his age. I saw him before he noticed me, but then his eyes met mine. He smiled and signaled a recognition. We met for a couple of moments later, away from the others, but did not say a word...at least not out loud. We touched our hands to each other. And then he was gone.

But with a promise.

☼

A few months after he left, I met his mother. We saw each other at a wedding of one of my priestess sisters, and we looked at each other with that flash of acknowledgement that lets each one of us know that this person, this meeting was something special. Mary had wisdom far beyond her years, even without any formal training. She was extraordinary. We did not speak then, but, as with her son, I knew I would see her again.

If there was such a thing as a Mother of God, she would've been it. We are all children of God, however, as Yeshua said repeatedly. How this got so blown up to mean that he was the only Son of God that ever lived and would ever live, I will never truly understand... except that it was part of the plan of the time for him to be deemed divine, and so he was and no one else could be. But why those people lived in such fear that they had to cast a shadow of shame and dishonor over humanity by letting one person reign as divine while the rest of us are unworthy worms of the dust is what is so mystifying. Fear need not take control anymore.

Oh, but I digress yet again. I might do that a lot—there is so much I want to tell you. Back to beloved Mary, the ostensible Mother of God. She was a teacher of teachers. She was a wisdomkeeper for wisdomkeepers. She knew. She shined. She was so kind, but she could have a bite when she wanted to. With teeth...sharp teeth. She also had a keen sense of the whole picture, and she knew what was coming in her life and in the life of her son. But for this time, her heart was not pondering; it was joyous and free, as it was almost all of the time that I knew her...with one major exception, as you can well imagine.

Yeshua told me many, many times that, while he came in knowing much of what he later transmitted and he learned much from his travels to the East, most of what he taught he learned from his mother. When he was a child and would complain about the state of something, she would say, "You're the one in charge of how you feel about it, my darling. And you can't change anything from the state of mind that you're in right now." Or on their journey back to Israel when he was pining for a friend he had had to leave in Egypt, she taught him how to meet the friend on the inner planes. Or he would hurt himself, and she would lay her hands on his wound; when she pulled her hands away, the wound would be completely healed.

Mary learned this information from her own mother, Anna, who in turn learned it from her mother, and along the matriarchal lineage all the way back to ancient Egyptian times and to her formidable ancestor Isis—not the Goddess Isis of myth, but the woman that the myth was based on. The myth of those ancient, ancient times was of a virgin birth to a divine son. Sound familiar? The hieroglyphics of old even show the mother and son with halos around their heads. Many stories have been recycled over the years, yes? The important thing is to remember that they are *stories*... certainly nothing to base a prejudicial thought on, much less a revolution or crusade.

Mary would be the first to tell anyone that she was no virgin. And Joseph, her husband, certainly would have taken issue with that denotation. A virgin mother! Where does that leave sexuality in the whole scheme of things? Yes, I suppose she was deemed far purer that way. Sexuality and giving birth are two of the most sacred functions in life...interesting how the two main women in Yeshua's life were bestowed the complete opposite and unreachable traits a woman could have: A virgin mother. A whore. I understand that many men can have a virgin/whore complex, but this is ridiculous.

☼

In the beginning, Elohim...as the Hebrew texts state. Elohim is plural, and the root of the word is feminine...so in the beginning of the use of the word for God, they understood the dual nature of God, of Life—the masculine and the feminine. Somehow half of the whole was extinguished. Part of Yeshua's work was to restore the divine feminine to its holy, holy place next to the divine masculine in the story of creation.

As I said in the beginning of this chronicle to you, a long time ago people were scared, and they created many rules and regulations based on that fear. Of the many things that frightened them, one of the most prominent was the power of a woman. To bear and then be able to feed another human life is quite remarkable. But it was fearsome, even to women at times, which might have been the reason some women were so ready to surrender their natural power. We had the matriarchy a long, long time ago. We've had the patriarchy for a long, long time now. It is Her time to return—not as a matriarchy again but in partnership with Him. The two, together...at long last. We are coming to the time of partnership, a time of balance, a time when we exalt in the gifts and strengths of each one of us, knowing that everyone brings something essential to the whole of creation.

☼

My own mother died just before Yeshua's return, and as he and I grew close together, Mary stepped in as a matriarchal elder and teacher for me. My mother and I loved each other very much, but she and I did not travel in the same realms and so we were never especially close. She was very surprised when I was chosen to be taught at the temples and palaces of the priestesses. Sometimes the family of our childhood is the last to sense who we truly are, and we often create our own new families as we come of age, comprised of people who may be unrelated to us but who understand us and travel where we do.

Actually, there was nothing outwardly special about me, not that I revealed to my family and friends anyway, so I am not surprised that my mother was so surprised. As a child I would watch the energy field around a flower emanate light. I would watch the colors dance over people's heads—bright when they were happy, dark when they were sad, shooting angry rays when they were upset or being dishonest. I would lie in bed watching entities over my head shift shapes and float on currents of air, even when no wind was blowing. But I kept all that to myself. No one else ever talked about such things, and so I did not either. When the High Priestesses came to ask for me, my mother suggested they take my older sisters, or even my younger brother, as boys were sometimes welcome, too. But they had come for me. They found me in their dreamtime and were led to me by signs, the way they find all the priestesses of the temple. When they found me, they recognized me, the way we all recognize a kindred spirit when we see one.

So, since my mother and I were not journeying the same path, Mary became the mother who could teach me. But I am moving ahead of myself here yet again. I have so very much I want to tell you, and I seem to be tripping over my own words. Back to Yeshua and the time before he came back to me.

There was not a moment where he was far from my thoughts, not in a sense of longing but in a sense of profound, loving connection. I spent my days in deep, deep prayer and meditation, attending to my tasks and chores, improving my healing, teaching the young women and girls under my tutelage, but my nights were spent preparing for him, whether or not I was with someone else...for if I was with someone, our activities were preparing me for him...and if I was alone my thoughts were preparing me for him. My education and preparation grew as I heard teachings of the esoteric sciences and the sublime from the nighttime sky, from the gentle breezes through the gardens, from the unspoken transmissions by the unseen wise ones, and from the Earth herself.

There was so much to fill a day. A healer's first job is to realize that there is nothing to heal, only an attitude to maintain. Have you ever heard of those people who have many different personalities within one physical body? Sometimes one personality can be withdrawn, inhibited, fearful, and her countenance reflects that. Another personality can be outgoing, flamboyant, joyous, and her countenance reflects that. Another part of her can be very, very ill, and the body registers that while the other personalities suffer absolutely no effects of that illness, and the body does not register the illness when the healthy personalities are forward. How very strange, considering they reside in the same body! Why would one part have that illness and another part not show any sign of such a disease? Well, it just shows the disease is in the mind, not the body. So there is nothing to heal—only a decision to be made, a realization to arrive at, and a remembrance to return to.

The healer's second job is to learn to maintain that high-level, positive attitude, which is very difficult in a world where most people insist on sickness, depravity, poverty, famine, the whole negative gamut. So if a thought of judgment came into my mind, I had to dispel it. If a thought of unkindness came up within me, I had to transform it. How many judgments and thoughts of unkindness do you have during a day? Well, I did, too. All right, maybe not as many, because I was trained since adolescence to stay with the positive and avoid the negative. But the mystics of the eastern land sit for years and years dispelling the voices that arise in them—and there are always even further places to go inside to rout out subtle yet deeply entrenched voices. The healers of the lands to the south spend years learning their work, and there is always more to learn. Everyone on Earth has pain, fear, doubts, limits; no one is exempt. The mystics and great teachers might have less and less, but then they also go to deeper levels to explore and seek out more areas to transform than most others are even aware of, let alone travel to. Everyone's—but especially the healer's—job is to overcome negativity, at deeper and deeper places within us, at more and more subtle levels, so that no matter what happens in our outer experience, we are centered, whole, positive, and an uplifting example of a life well lived.

There was a very steep hill just outside the city walls. When I first arrived and found myself with some free time, somewhat of a luxury, I would climb the hill to look at my new city—a city I loved from the first moment I arrived. My breathing would be fast and heavy, since I was not used to this kind of exertion. Over time I was able to climb the hill more easily, until

I reached the point where my breathing would remain nearly steady as I approached the summit and perhaps I would take one big breath of air at the top of the hill— no more fast and heavy breathing for many minutes, as with my early climbs. But fitness is not just a physical attribute; there is spiritual fitness, too. When I first arrived at the temple palace, small events and minor issues would upset me. Over time I found myself returning to the peace of my center faster and faster. It does not matter what happens in life, only what our reaction is and how quickly we can return to the peace of the stillness within ourselves. Mastery is not routing out all bad events of life, for no one can do that; mastery is a rapid return to the still center point, despite the wild ride that can be this life of ours.

In addition to being very aware, I was also very sick as a young child. Many healers have been sick themselves. We very often teach what we need to learn or what we have overcome, so we can teach from our own experience. I overcame my illnesses more through thought and communing with the Divine than through anything elemental, like herbs and ointments— although they can make the healing and the healer's job more fun...at least more tactile, textured, and aromatic, if nothing else.

Far into the future from my day but now here in your day, the people of science have ways to see what the mystical teachers have always known...that the things that make up one person are the things that make up another, are the things that make up the rocks, are the things that make up the stars that burn in the nighttime sky, are the foods that we eat, are the waters of the world, are the animals of the plains, are the dust floating in the air, are the new babies being born at this moment, are the tired old bodies passing on at this moment, are the salts of our tears, are the salts of the oceans, are the sounds of the winds, are the beatings of our hearts.

Nothing ever, ever leaves or dies—it only changes shape and appearance. It lives on one side of the veil or another, in this dimension or another, on this planet or another, but it is not really much different.

Most people do not know any of this. But it is not their fault. We are all excellent students—no matter what our intelligence level—and our lessons depend on who our teachers have been, what they have been taught, and how long we have been taught the particular lessons...plus how ready we are to learn something new when a new teacher with a new lesson appears. Most tend to live under a spell. Politicians and people in power have learned this, often to the detriment of those in their sphere of influence. They can cast the spells further, too, although I do not mean in the form of black magic—I mean in creating a mass hysteria or anything else they want in order to pursue their private schemes on a public level.

I hear many of you repeating the same pessimistic mantra that you told yourself yesterday, and the day before, and the day before that, and even eighteen lifetimes ago. And *you* are the lightworkers! Stop it! And I am not the only one who can hear you—everyone on the planet can hear you, whether they know it or not, especially those right around you. And imagine what those who have not had their hearts and eyes and ears opened are thinking and how it is affecting everyone. But you cannot afford the extravagance of dwelling in negative thought, not even for a moment. All right, indulge yourself, if you must, for a moment here and there, just as you must let grief and devastation consume you for a short time in order for them to pass. Move it through you and out of you, as quickly as you can. But do not dwell there—it is not fair to the rest of creation. It is time to break the cycle. There is a reason that so many people use prayer beads and mantras and chants—to train their minds out of the normal routine that we humans can find ourselves in, to break their own personal spells and reverse a possible downward spiral.

If you have picked up this book, I would take it to mean that you are more perceptive, more intuitive, more open than most. Probably much of what I have to say are things you already know. But it is always good to be reminded. And then be reminded again. And then again. And....

We can look at our brothers and sisters who are caught under the spell the same way the Beloved looks at us. And how does the Beloved look at us? Only through the eyes of love. That is it. Nothing else. There is nothing we can do that would make the Beloved love us less. It should be the same with the healer and those who come to her for healing. It should be the same with our partners, but unfortunately, even in the best of partnerships, this is not always the case. And if we track it back to its origin, a misalignment of love with our true love is because one of us lost track of who we are...one of us went back to the spell, even for just a moment.

It is our job to keep ourselves centered, grounded, and positive and to cast out doubt, fear, negativity wherever it abides. And then be a model for each one of our brothers and sisters.

No, I did not say it would be quick and easy! Did you hear me say it would be quick and easy?

☼

My beloved. One of the first things any spiritual master learns is to think of everything in terms of the

Beloved, especially the beloved creator of all that is. And one of the delightful ways we can experience the love of the creator is with our beloved partner. And by bearing our own children, as the mother creator bears us. And by awakening to the love in our neighbors, and then to the love in strangers, and then to the love in our so-called enemies. Throwing our arms around those we love is like being able to throw our arms around God/ Goddess/All That Is. Sometimes it is easier to love a stranger or an enemy from a higher level than from the Earth plane, but after a while even down here it becomes easier.

My beloved. He and I would talk to each other in this way all the time, in our thoughts, for those many years we were apart, and then out loud almost every moment we were together. Life is a celebration of the Beloved in oh its many forms.

My beloved. I am talking to you now. You are my beloved. Always.

☼

So, no, I did not miss him—not really. I took every moment as an opportunity to extend myself. I did not know when he would return, only that he would.

It was almost a decade.

# CHAPTER 3

I could always tell when I had been dreaming about him, because I woke up smiling and my body would be tingling more than usual. The day of his return I woke up with my entire body on fire. As I sat down to my early meditation, my heart was dancing and my spirit was soaring through the ethers. I knew he was close. As I finished breakfast and started preparing the day's lessons for my students, my inner eye saw him approaching the villages on the outskirts of Jerusalem.

Later that day I was returning from the market with one of my priestess sisters. While we had many servants to perform the chores for the palace, we often cooked, cleaned, and shopped ourselves, as well. Every task can be a meditation, a prayer, an avenue of awakening. *Every* task. Plus, it does the world no good whatsoever if we develop ourselves to carry more and more light and knowledge and then tuck ourselves away somewhere, hidden in the rafters of life. I always found the market a particularly great place to have my patience tried, and then to be a better emanatress of light for it, both in the moment and beyond.

He and I arrived at the temple gate at the same time, from different directions. He almost disappeared in the haze of my tears. My sister rescued the parcels that were slipping from my arms and quickly vanished.

He and I looked at each other, put our hands together in prayer position, raised them so that the base of the thumb was directly over the third eye, and bowed gently, slowly to each other. This is the meeting of high spirit to high spirit, and a deep acknowledgement of the Divine both within each other and everywhere.

Then he quickly took my hands in his and held them to his heart. "My Mary," he whispered.

"Yeshua."

"Did you hear me talking to you?"

"Yes. Every day."

"Every day was a step closer to you."

"Yes."

"My Mary, my beloved."

"My beloved Yeshua."

☼

I had known so many people in such a myriad of fashions. I was prepared for most of my life to be with others to teach, to share, to heal. But this man, this union was something entirely different. Every moment with him was at once very familiar and yet at the same time was a door opening to a brand-new vista, something more than I had ever expected. It was sweeter than the sweet smell of land in the springtime, brighter than the brilliance of a shooting star, as welcome as a cool drink of water on a blazing hot day, more comfortable than my dearest friend, as graciously loving as the God/Goddess of my soul. My heart rejoiced that at long, long last we were together, and yet it felt like we had never been apart.

By this time, as one of the higher-ranking teachers, I had my own quarters on the palace grounds, and I took him there. My beautiful sitting room greeted us. Flowers filled the space, both cut flowers set in pottery around the room as well as flowers that adorned the multitudes of vines that entered through the doors, windows, and cracks in the foundation from the garden right outside. The aroma of the flowers, made even more pungent from the heat of the afternoon, was intoxicating—as if I needed anything else to add to the immense bliss that filled my heart.

A wash basin sat next to the doorway, with washing cloths nearby. I soaked a cloth in the cool water in the basin and then very carefully washed away the dust from his face. He rinsed another cloth and washed away the dust of the day from my face. Then he rinsed the cloth again, knelt before me, and washed my feet. More than just the day's debris from walking the dusty roads was washed away with his gentle strokes. I did the same for him, rinsing and washing away the years of travel from his brown feet, and welcoming him back to Jerusalem, to me...his home.

We sank onto a few of the cushions that filled my sitting room, just clasping each other's hands and staring into each other's eyes. His mouth slowly drew up at the corners into a lazy, slightly crooked smile and dimples formed in his cheeks. The sun glinted on the flecks of red in his dark hair. My hair cascaded down my back in thick and unruly curls and waves of black. His hair, equally thick but straighter, fell to just past his shoulders and seemed to hold numerous colors of the Earth: black, brown, red, and auburn. Even among the pungent aromas of the flowers, herbs, oils, and ointments in my quarters, I could smell his scent—of the Earth.

Finally he wrapped his arms around me and held me, for hours. The breeze carried the aroma of cooking, and we heard the rise and fall of voices as my temple family prayed and then chattered as they enjoyed the evening meal. We heard the birds performing their closing songs of the day as the sun disappeared and cool came to the land. A hush fell over the temple and the city as night descended. We fell asleep together, and when I awoke in the morning he was gone.

☼

I was very old, for the time, for a woman who had not married and had children. He was very old, too, for the time, for a man who had not married and had children. On the palace grounds, however, we were not such an abnormality as we were out on the streets of Jerusalem. Many of my sisters married and left the compound, taking the teachings into everyday family life; but many stayed there and remained single, choosing to focus on teaching the new girls. I had not mentioned him to any of my temple family for all those years, but he was accepted immediately, without even one word, as my partner. The temple High Priest and Priestess asked to perform our wedding ceremony, and the preparations commenced.

But the ceremony was only a formality...we were already married. Plus, the temple would make any excuse for a festivity.

☼

For a week after his return he would join me after the evening meal and just sit with me, holding me, sometimes talking of his adventures, sometimes asking about the routine of the temple and the lessons I had taught that day. We would fall asleep together, but he would be gone by the time I awoke in the morning.

But one night, after this week of exhibiting as much patience as I possibly could, I did not fall asleep as usual. It was time. His eyes teased me as he smiled his slightly crooked smile.

"Your eyes sparkle like jewels," he whispered.

"As do yours." Truly, I thought, mine must have paled in comparison to his, but perhaps not, judging by the way he studied my eyes. And the person we draw to us is always our greatest mirror.

I took him by the hand and led him into the sleeping area of my quarters. I had been awaiting this moment for years, but the moment could wait a little longer. We sat on the cushions at the foot of my bed, our legs folded under us, knees just touching. We lay our hands on our knees, palms up, with the tips of our fingers barely touching. I stared into his eyes and watched as the entire world, including his body and mine, faded away, except for the blazing orbs that were those two amazing eyes. I always knew that we are light beings wrapped up in a casing of skin, and this moment was living proof—clearly showing it to me even more. His face would reappear from time to time, in differing shapes and colors and textures. Even when our bodies returned to my vision, I still saw the light that was his eyes as well as the burning flame above his head. I knew that he saw mine as well, judging by the upward cast of his eyes every few moments.

He reached for me and held me in his arms, gazing into my eyes. In the soft, flickering light of the oil lamp, his eyes were unlike any others I had ever seen—they glowed, alight with something from another world... giant pools of shimmering love and light.

"I have never seen eyes like yours," he whispered.

"Did you know that is what I was thinking about yours?" I laughed.

"Of course. But it is not another world. They are from this world, only...." His voice trailed off. "You know there are two kinds of people?" he asked.

"Yes."

"Tell me."

"Those who know and those who do not know that they know yet."

He smiled. "Someone taught you well."

"As they did you."

He pulled me to him and I felt his body pressing against mine. He explored my face with his lips—my cheeks, my forehead, my eyelids. I felt my body relax as I surrendered to his arms, his soft caresses, the gentle sweep of his hand through my hair, the press of his body against mine.

There was no hurry. There was no other time. There was only now.

I ran my fingers over his face, tracing his cheekbones, his jawline, his eyebrows. How many men had trained me for this moment and how many men had I trained? Yet there had been no one else before, not really. Not like this. No one else had ever touched me—my heart and spirit—in this way.

His lips met mine and a jolt passed through my entire body. His tongue explored my mouth. I inhaled his scent and reveled in the taste of him. He tasted like the place where the desert meets the waters—sand and salt and hot with cool relief. As our tongues pressed together, I heard a hum. All the sounds of the temple and city disappeared, enfolded into the hum buzzing through my head. There was no other sensation in my body except at the tip of my tongue, where it met his.

After a few moments I moved my hands over his back, his shoulders, his arms. His skin was firm yet soft, yielding, just like his lips. No other man had felt like this. The effects of years of travel, sunshine, even hard work whenever necessary were as nothing on him. It was as though he was made of stone yet covered with a thick, taut wrapping of the softest, finest fabric.

His hands started to explore my body, still shrouded by my garments. I unfastened the ties down the front of my robes; he pushed them off my shoulders and they fell to the floor. His eyes brightened even more, and he smiled as he looked at my body in the light of the oil lamp. I absolutely loved my body. It certainly was not perfect, but no body ever is—although in the dim light, it appeared pretty near perfect. I had large breasts, still fairly tight and high on my chest because I had not had children. My hips and rump were well-rounded but my belly was flat. My body was neither too round nor too thin. It was probably so beautiful because I adored it so much, relished moving around in it, delighted in the senses of it—from catching a tangy drop of fruit on my tongue, to smelling the aromas of life in the temple and life on the streets of Jerusalem, to the thrill of lovemaking. I never understood how so many people, women especially, could disparage their own bodies—a beautiful vehicle no matter what the shape and size. There is no such thing as an ugly body. But the more we love our bodies, the more they will be what society terms beautiful. Of course the love must start in the depths of us, well under any exterior.

I pulled off his clothing. I had not a vestige of shyness or modesty after all my training in the art of passion as well as education in the unparalleled majesty of the body. He had none either. He was an amazingly beautiful man with an amazingly beautiful body, luscious even, and he had neither a shred of hesitation nor undue pride about showing it to me. He picked me up and placed me on the bed. He ran his fingers over my belly and breasts, stroking, teasing, igniting a fire in me. His mouth explored my neck, my breasts, my belly. I pulled him back up to my face and kissed him as my legs wrapped around his middle, my arms wrapped around his shoulders, pulling, pushing him closer to the inside of my body and the inside of my being. He lay on top of me, filling me up—body, mind, soul, spirit.

He rubbed the top of my head, my crown, with gentle strokes, the same way he was rubbing the center of my fire with another part of him. My body arched as a hot current coursed through my being, and I saw a blinding flash of light. A scream escaped from deep inside me. This activity was not physical, this was not even spiritual—this was beyond anything I had ever experienced. The whole of the cosmos was dancing in my soul. There was no separation between his body and mine, between the sky and me, between the planet and me, between eternity and me.

The ultimate moment came for both of us at the same time. Our eyes were open and we stared into each other's soul. There was a fireburst of energy, like a million shooting stars, coming from his eyes and around the top of his head, and I could feel the same coming from me to him.

My body trembled with ecstasy. I could not speak. For many moments there was only the sound of my gasps of breath mingled with his. I inhaled the musky scent of bodies spent in the making of love.

"Someone certainly taught you well," I finally whispered, laughing at my understatement.

"As they did you." He also laughed.

My heart was cracked wide open, ready to receive words, messages, ideas from other realms, including some I did not want. I felt a tremor as my heart warned me against opening too much, against the possibility of the tremendous pain that can accompany huge, expansive openings of the mind, body, soul, and spirit. I quickly tried to assure myself that there was only now, only this moment, lying in his arms. But the tremor flickered again.

"Whatever it is, I will be able to handle it," I said to my heart, silently. "Just let me have this time right now."

"We are never given anything we are not prepared for," he whispered.

"Yes." Sometimes it was not always convenient to be with someone who can read minds so clearly...and there were certainly times over our years together that he felt the same way about me.

"Just a gentle reminder."

"Yes."

As we drifted off to sleep, the tremor was quelled by the thrill of being with him and the magic of our time with each other. I smiled as I finally heard the music for the first time...from no instruments that were of this world.

☼

The next morning I found myself picking at the breakfast brought by Rachel, my maidservant. How in the world had she known to bring two plates? Why was I even asking? She was as awake and aware as Yeshua was, as I was, but she wanted to spend her life literally serving, as a servant, for me. She was the happiest person I had ever met, other than my beloved, and I loved her as much as I loved anyone in that lifetime, except for Yeshua, his mother, and one other person. She was the epitome of what Yeshua later said to many of his students: The *"greatest among you shall be your servant."* He didn't literally mean a maidservant when he said that, of course; Yeshua spoke in metaphors. But that was the case with our beloved Rachel.

I had to ask him. "How did you learn so well? Who taught you? Do you still love her? Or them?"

I could not believe the questions that were springing out of my mouth! Had I really just asked him so directly? But I had to know. I already knew in my heart, but my mind had to be assuaged as well. The sun flooded the room, lighting him up even more. He devoured his breakfast in just a couple of minutes, which was understandable, considering the appetite we both had worked up. But my hunger was on hold until I heard his answers.

"Mary," he laughed, "those are quite the questions you are asking, my beautiful love."

"Forgive me," I sighed. "But you know I have been formally trained, and to pass this training on. Where–"

My questions stopped at the look of pain on his face. But the pain of loss quickly transformed into the joy of remembering. And he told me.

He was not intimate with a woman until his early twenties, when he had journeyed far along the Silk Way. Immediately upon his arrival to a small town slightly off the Way, where he had been intuitively led, he was brought to a palace.

The king greeted him and said, "You are finally here. You have traveled far to learn much, this I know."

"Yes," Yeshua responded.

"I want you to meet my daughter."

"But I am not staying here, in this land," Yeshua told the man.

"Yes, I understand," was the answer. "But if you are to be a teacher of the people, there is far more to learn than just the ways of the holy man."

"How he knew what my future was going to be, I did not know," Yeshua told me, "but by this time of my life very little surprised me any more."

A great ceremony followed, celebrating his arrival. Apparently he had been expected by more than just the king. The princess was brought to him amidst cacophonous music-making and dancing and festivities. She was several years younger, extremely beautiful, and recognized throughout the region for a very special gift in her spirit. She wore red robes with red jewels and red flowers through her long black hair. Yeshua wore a robe of gold.

At night they were alone together. Neither of them had ever been with anyone in this way before, but it was as if they were already well familiar with the art of love.

His primary concern regarding her was what would happen to her once he left, which he knew he still had to do. She would already be considered as belonging to another man, at least in the view of the general populace, if not in the minds of her family and friends and the more open-minded members of their circle.

"It is as it should be," was her only answer. "I am to be with you, for right now. And that is more than enough for me."

"It was not as if I did not have a choice about this," Yeshua told me. "But it seemed pre-ordained somehow. There was something higher going on. And it was not as though I did not want to be with a woman, but I had not sought out the opportunity. I was quite busy learning the ways of the priests and monks, back in Israel and all along the way to the East."

"There must be a great many broken hearts and disappointed women between here and the East," I teased.

"I don't think so." His modesty was not false; while he was very awake and aware about subjects that most people on Earth cannot begin to comprehend, his beauty, sexual aura, and effect on women—over the age of two and with even remotely decent eyesight—was not really apparent to him.

"Sometimes people choose not to be opened in the sexual realms," I said, more to change the subject and to avoid suddenly sounding like a teenager with her first love, "because they want to concentrate on the spiritual realms only. But it's quite clear you chose to be opened on all levels."

"Yes."

There is a tremendous heart opening that happens in our passionate unions with another that cannot be replicated. Yes, many priests and monks and nuns choose to have that union only with the Divine, so their hearts may be opened in that realm, and that is their choice. But Yeshua was to be a teacher of the people, a bringer of light to the lower dimensions of living. Despite all claims to the contrary, mostly put forth by the various churches that came along that said they were in his name but were clearly (to us, now) not of his teaching and character, Yeshua was not a monk. He never chose to be celibate, as you can now obviously see.

I once met a man who told me he was celibate because he wanted to dedicate his life to serving God. While I honor everyone's journey, I was saddened by the choice he had made. We serve God in everything we do. And to retreat from the joys of the physical human body while we're actually fortunate and privileged enough to be in one seems to me to be a life only part lived.

"And of course that sort of thing is just not done. A woman does not give herself to a man who will leave. But she wanted to. Both she and her father had a dream that I was coming and that the events were to unfold the way they did."

"How long did you stay?"

"Just a few months."

"What happened when you left? Didn't she want you to stay?"

"Yes, but we both knew I had to go."

"Where is she now, do you know?" I asked.

"She went on to life beyond the veil," he answered. "I

discovered that on my journey back. And she had a child, who I never knew about until my return. He is being trained as a master teacher."

"You have a child!" Countless emotions tripped over each other, filling my heart—but I was not certain which emotion was primary for me regarding this news.

"Yes."

"Why didn't you stay with him?"

"He is being very well taken care of. Everything worked out well, as it should have, because I was to come back here...and return to you."

I blinked away my tears and he kissed me. The emotions in my heart blended into one: gratitude...for this woman who had loved him, for this son who carried his father's body and soul through his own body and soul into the next generations...and for me.

"So she went on to perform some greater work somewhere else, I am sure," he said.

"Well, she performed a great work with you!" I laughed. "So, um......... and....... then?" I paused.

"Who else? Is that what you are asking?"

I started to speak and then paused again. I nodded and he laughed with me, at my silliness.

"No one. Until you."

Unbelievable. Absolutely, totally unbelievable. My mind tried to wrap itself around the words he had just spoken. He was certainly a true master in more than just the ways he became famous for.

"And to think, you could have been a king," I teased him, mostly to take the emphasis off the blushing burn that started to spread across my face. Good Goddess! When was the last time I had blushed? Probably two-thirds of my lifetime ago. I gazed at him. He was absolutely gorgeous, and his beauty was even more enhanced by the light that radiated from within him and around him.

"You know something? I think even the sun is basking in you this morning," he smiled.

I shook my head, trying not to be so stunned by his mind-reading abilities.

"You are so beautiful," he whispered to me. "Just look at the light coming off of you, from you."

There certainly was not going to be a way of hiding anything from him. I cast my eyes down; the light and love beaming from his eyes was more than even I could handle in that moment. He patiently waited for me to look up again, where his eyes met mine and smiled at me, compelling my heart to expand and open to places it never thought it would reach.

"Well, you already are a king, my king," I whispered.

"My queen."

# CHAPTER 4

The temple came alive, even more than its usual full bustle of activity, with the preparations for our wedding. Oh, the flowers! Oh, the people! Oh, the food! Oh, the cleaning!

I don't think the temple had ever been so scoured and scrubbed. Every student, every teacher, every servant scrubbed, mopped, polished for over a week. Former students and friends of the temple came from near and far to assist the temple in gleaming and sparkling. The food started arriving by the bushel basket days before the ceremony to feed the multitudes of helpers and keep them sustained for their tasks.

Yeshua and I were forbidden to assist in any way, not even for a moment. Since my students were put to work, I had no classes to teach, so he and I spent the days in my quarters. When the idleness grew too great for us, we took walks to the hills outside of the city. The beautiful garden, Gethsemane, called us back to her quiet shade amongst the olive trees again and again, day after day. On our way back to the temple, we would stroll through the marketplace, and I noticed women, young and old and everywhere in between, glancing at him, again and again, day after day.

"Do you notice the men watching you?" he asked me one afternoon.

Men? What men? "No." Despite all the love I had shared, there was only one recipient of my passion now. The others had disappeared into the ethers. "Do you see the women watching you?"

"No."

I found that very hard to believe, but he certainly

would never say something untrue. This humble modesty coming from inside his spectacularly beautiful form was a powerful aphrodisiac for me.

Back in our room he took me in his arms. "Thank you, beloved Mother Father God, for the most wonderful woman in the world—a woman every man in this city would love to call his wife. And I'm the one who can do that!"

I found myself being extremely grateful that he could completely ignore the longing glances of the women in the streets. Perhaps it was a prelude to his years of teaching; sometimes the ability to be totally present but not emotionally available was important. I had long ago learned to not look directly at men in the streets for longer than a fraction of a second because sometimes they would consider a friendly look as an invitation to them. But I did my best to spread upliftment as often as I could, wherever I went. There have certainly been many spiritual leaders over the centuries and even today who cannot separate their important work from their human longings. Such longings are natural, of course, and they can be met in the right time, in the right place, with the right person. To use one's position to increase time in the bedroom and increase the number of bedmates—just because they can—is not work well done.

But the people in the streets of Jerusalem were appreciative of something, long after we walked by, and they were not even certain of what, or why.

☼

Oh, what a gift: to let their day be so much better than it was, because they came into contact with....
You.

The day after Yeshua returned to me, I asked the temple carpenters to construct a new bed for us. They did far more than just make us a new bed—they built an entirely brand-new bedroom on an entirely brand-new second floor. Now our quarters were as spacious as those of the Head Priest and Priestess, which I did not think was right, but no one heeded my protests. Just one level up, an extra twelve feet further into the heavens, enabled us to see over the temple walls for a truly magnificent view of the rooftops of Jerusalem as well as the hills in the distance, past the city walls. The large, airy room was filled with light streaming in from windows on all four sides—a great luxury.

As for the new bed, four sturdy posts stood guard around a giant cushion, which was made of a thick but very soft fabric and stuffed with lamb's wool, feathers, fabrics—anything and everything soft. It had several slits on all four sides, which opened into pockets that we filled with flower petals. Many a time, during that warm, wonderful place after sleep and before fully awakening, I'd wonder if I'd walked in my sleep to the gardens. And then I'd smile because the comfort was far too exquisite, and I'd remember that the garden had been brought to my bedroom. Could even Caesar's wife have had such a sumptuous bed?

The housekeepers and seamstresses stormed our quarters, and before we knew it, all of the curtains, cushions, and furnishings were taken from the lower rooms and divvied up to a number of the younger women on the temple grounds. Scores of new sitting cushions, draperies, pillows, coverings, fabrics, and wall hangings took their place. White (a completely impractical color for those days and times and climate and amount of dirt and sand flying through the streets) fabrics were draped from the bedposts and could be tied up during the day and opened at night to close off the outside world and create a little world of our own.

My rooms had been filled with gifts from all corners of the Earth, brought to me by students, both male and female. Stones, shells, jewels, weavings, drawings, pottery, and sculptures bedecked the walls and tabletops. These, too, went along with the furnishings and fabrics and filled the rooms of my sisters and students.

Our rooms were empty for about one and a half days before they started to fill up once more—again with beautiful things gathered from all corners of the Earth...only this time they were wedding gifts for the two of us. Packages started arriving with ornaments, pottery, vases, artwork, crafted animals—things made with so much love by people I had known and people who had encountered Yeshua on the road. New jewels, precious stones, and polished glass sparkled on the walls and tabletops and from the windows where they were hung to catch the morning and afternoon sunshine, allowing myriads of rainbows to dance around the room most of the day. Teas, spices, oils, ointments, perfumes, scents—oh, but they had been carried so far by someone at some point and now our quarters were filled with their pungent aromas. We were humbled and awestruck by the generosity of our friends and loved ones, as such precious, beautiful things were so rare in that time and place as well as far beyond the means of most people.

I'd always had a place to live, before. My mother and father's house was simple but more than enough for the family. The temple had been beyond the realm of most people in those days—my room had been fit for a king and queen. But I'd never had a true home before, and neither had he.

There had been so much activity, so much love and passion shared in my room heretofore. Now a new chapter of my life was beginning, a life of commitment to one. My life was now going to be about delving deeper rather than casting a wide net. Both had their benefits: My previous purpose had been to benefit as many as possible. Starting at this point and coming in its right time, more would be benefited from my union with my one, because of who he was.

And, yes, starting at this point and coming in its right time, more would be benefited from his union with his one, because of who I was.

☼

The customs for most weddings were very strict in our time—there were many events that only the men could participate in or only the women could be a part of; there were only certain foods that could be eaten, only certain items of clothing that could be worn. We had none of that. The High Priestess and High Priest of the temple, husband and wife themselves, officiated over the ceremony, and they created a special ritual just for us. We composed our own vows.

I was sequestered in our quarters the morning of our wedding, while Yeshua was taken to a special chapel for his preparations. A dozen girls doted over me, seeing to every detail of my preparations.

At the appointed hour my gaggle of girls accompanied me to the main temple square. Over a thousand people had thronged to the temple for our wedding. All of my students and their families, both old family members as well as the new families of their own creation, all of my temple sisters and their families, my own extended family from Magdala, Yeshua's mother and his brothers and sisters and their families were present. Even a number of friends and acquaintances he met on his journey arrived in town to join us to celebrate our joy. As I walked across the large square, I recognized face after face in the crowd—beautiful, beaming smiles wishing me nothing but the utmost of happiness and knowing that I had found it. I saw the shimmering face of his beautiful, beloved mother—oh, how she was so adored by Yeshua and his brothers and sisters as well as this newcomer to her family...his beloved mother who was now my beloved mother— beaming as she welcomed me with all her heart as one of her own.

Garlands of flowers hung across the entrance and the entire ceiling of the large, open-sided temple hall, where the ceremony, dinner, and festivities were to take place. Baskets of flowers stood by every doorway and building column while more flowers bedecked every table that was laden with mountains of food.

Across the square, on a dais, stood my beloved, patiently waiting for me. The High Priestess and Priest stood by him. For a moment the entire crowd disappeared and just the luminescent light that was my soon-to-be-husband was the only thing I could see. I walked toward the radiance that was this man I loved, who was joining his life with mine, in front of so many.

When I reached the dais he held his hand out and helped me walk up the three steps. His beautiful brown eyes glowed, with the soft edges crinkling.

"Mary, my love," he whispered, "you are a vision of love, light, and beauty."

"As are you, my darling."

A soft throat clearing from the High Priestess brought our attention off of each other and back to the main event at hand.

"Mary and Yeshua," Alana, the Priestess said, "you are coming together in one of the most sacred contracts that two people can enter into. And yet, as every one of us gathered here knows, you are already there."

I barely heard what she said. I only saw the burning orbs of light that were my beloved's eyes, the flame of love and light shooting over his head, and the iridescent luminosity radiating around his entire being. The world had faded away and his being of light was in full brilliance. The air around us was electric.

"Mary and Yeshua," Andress, the Priest said, "We have come together to bless your union. But your union blesses each one of us as well."

"The love you both so obviously have for and display to each other," Alana said, "is a gift to God/Goddess/All That Is and a gift to all who know you and all who will encounter you in the years to come."

Alana blinked away tears. She was one of the High Priestesses who had come for me so many years before and had been training me to follow in her lead and to take her place when she left this Earth and crossed over. She had watched me grow and frequently told me that the highest gift a student can ever give her teacher is to surpass her. I never told her that I did not think I would be there long enough to take her place. Some things remain best unsaid, but she knew now that something much larger than either of us had ever envisioned was unfolding.

Alana and Andress were arrayed in resplendent robes of royal purple, which represented Spirit, and with sashes around their waists of green, blue, red, and white, which represented Earth, Water, Fire, and Air.

Yeshua's and my raiment were robes of white—a white so bright it defied the dust and grit that hung in the air, despite the large number of palms that had been so carefully laid over the temple grounds, especially over the aisle that I had just walked. Sashes of white circled our waists. Tiny white flowers dotted my hair, which cascaded over my shoulders and down my back.

Andress reached to the altar behind him and pulled forward two small pottery containers of soil, plus an urn. He handed us each one of the containers.

"Please place your soil into the urn," he instructed and we complied.

Alana reached behind her and brought forward two cups of water and handed a cup to each of us.

"Please pour from your vessel into the one."

Andress positioned a very large candle—very rare in those days—in the mixture of soil and water and gathered two candles from the altar. We each lit the one from our two, and we kept our own burning as well.

"And for air," Alana said, "remembering that we are creations of Earth, made of water, beings of fire, please speak your vows to each other.

"Mary, my beloved, my counterpart, I share with you my heart, I share with you my body, I share with you my soul, I share with you my spirit. And I share with you my today, my tomorrow, my eternity."

"Yeshua, my beloved, my counterpart, I share with you my heart, I share with you my body, I share with you my soul, I share with you my spirit. And I share with you my today, my tomorrow, my eternity."

"Speaking of eternity, the circle of a ring is a symbol of eternity," Andress stated, breaking into the long stare that Yeshua and I had become lost in. "Please share your rings as your statement of eternal commitment to each other."

Yeshua placed a band of gold on my third finger. The ancient Egyptians believed that an artery from that finger flows straight to the heart, and that is how the custom of wedding rings worn on that particular finger began. The ring was hot from being held in his hand, and I could very well feel the heat traveling to my heart, bringing a flush to my entire body.

"Mary, my beloved, I share with you my life, given to me by God/Goddess/All That Is. I lift up our union to celebrate our own lives and our life together, for our own glory and to glorify the One who created us."

I placed a gold band on his third finger, as well.

"Yeshua, my beloved, I share with you my life, given to me by God/Goddess/All That Is. I lift up our union to celebrate our own lives and our life together, for our own glory and to glorify the One who created us."

Alana continued after our vow, with something we did not expect. "Mary and Yeshua, one of the most important reasons that two people come together is to create a family. Another important reason is to do work that would remain undone if the two did not join together. And sometimes it is both."

She handed me a shell with a pearl placed inside, both very carefully brought from an ocean's side so far away.

"This represents the beings that you may bring into this world."

I was moved beyond words and my hands trembled around the gift she placed in my hands. I had long ago given up the idea of bearing a child and instead devoted my maternal energies to my students, who now numbered into the hundreds. Also I was well past the normal child-bearing age. The little shell and pearl blurred as tears filled my eyes.

This was a very special lifetime, mine was, but that did not mean I was beyond the natural desires of the human life. A glimmer of hope started inside that perhaps I was not too old and not too committed to other services to have a child myself. Yeshua smiled at me.

Andress handed Yeshua a golden cruciform, the Egyptian symbol representing the joining of Heaven and

Earth. "And this, my dear beloveds, is for the work you will do together, that will serve us all."

"Thank you for what you have come to give us," Alana said to both of us.

The priest and priestess raised their hands in the holy prayer position to their foreheads; Yeshua and I did likewise. The power swirling from my head to my hands and over to his head and hands and back was palpable, a life form of its own. Yeshua obviously felt the same thing, and we looked into each other's eyes for another long moment.

Suddenly I found myself picked up, wrapped up in his arms as he swirled and whirled me around and around, his lips planted on mine. The crowd went completely crazy.

I found myself hoping the Roman guards outside the temple caught the bliss in the roar. There were enough plants inside the temple walls who would inform them of the exact sequence of events and put their own interpretation on them, later. I hoped they were enjoying themselves in the meantime.

☼

Oh, the food! We generally did not eat much at one time, but the tables were loaded with legs of lamb and other roasted meats, flatbread and special breads, a myriad of fruits, jugs of water, jugs of wine, and an enormous wedding cake. I could practically taste the aroma wafting through the air. We ate and ate and ate. I also turned every morsel to light, turned every morsel to light, and turned every morsel to light. As humans we can generally eat whatever we want, provided we know it serves us. For the times when we want to eat something that doesn't serve our bodies, we can remember that anything we eat, any time, can be turned to light. That does not give us all permission to go on an eating frenzy, however! But eating whatever we want a few days here and there is all right.

The music and dancing continued until the streak of light appeared in the east, announcing that another day had come, much as we were loath that our wedding day was over. We retired to our quarters, far too exhausted and too exhilarated to sleep. A few hours later, well after the sun was halfway through its morning sojourn across the sky, Rachel brought our breakfast plates and found us still wide awake, recounting and remembering the events of the previous day to each other.

"It was the most beautiful ceremony I've ever witnessed," Rachel said. "It's as though you two gave everyone a glimpse of the possible—that true love, real joy, meeting another person on multiple levels...is actually possible."

She slipped from the room before we could respond.

We picked at our plates, but neither of us was hungry. Yeshua wrapped his arms around me and we finally started to drift off to sleep.

BANG! BANG! Our drifting was abruptly interrupted by a very loud noise, along with peals of laughter, right outside our quarters.

We ran to the window, where we were greeted by the sight of Eres, the band leader, joyfully banging on his drum. The other musicians circled around him, instruments poised and ready to play.

"Now don't be starting that family-making stuff so early," Eres called. "You have more dancing to do!"

The pipes and flutes and lyres started to play as beautiful voices started to sing to us, coaxing us from our room.

☼

The musicians and guests stayed for several more days, so the festivities—including hours and hours of dancing late into the night—continued.

And the food kept coming! There was far more than enough food flowing, from early morning to late night. I have no idea where it all came from and who was buying it for us, but many farmers and merchants must have been quite overjoyed with their sales at the marketplace that week.

The young priestesses honored us and the crowds with veil dances, circle dances, and dances I had never seen before—choreographed beauty and grace passed on from distant lands.

Yeshua smiled at a young student who danced and playfully flirted with him from behind her veil. Another young woman pushed her aside, practically causing her to trip over herself, and took her place. She raised her eyebrows and gave a few coy, seductive glances to him as she danced. She cast somewhat envious looks in my direction. Yeshua smiled at her, as well, with a smile that let her know that she, too, will find her king one day.

On the fourth day the musicians finally packed up their instruments, and the last of the crowd left, marking the end of our wedding celebration—at least the formal celebration. Our own informal celebration would continue nearly every moment we were together.

☼

Every time we made love at night, it was always by the light of our beautiful ceremonial oil lamp.

Well, almost always....

# CHAPTER 5

I might be a little biased, but ours was the kind of love that people dream about—the kind of love that is written about by poets, regaled about in tales by traveling storytellers, and sung about in both delightfully haunting and joyous melodies—but that most people never reach in their lifetime. Ours was so deep, so wide, so high. The second before his name even came to my mind, my lips were smiling and my heart was expanding.

Lovers give one of the greatest gifts to the world. Every couple that is madly, deeply, wildly, passionately, magnificently in love probably feels like they invented love. They didn't—we did! Just jesting...every couple invents their own love and it grows, or not, according to their needs and desires as well as the true purpose of their earthly journey.

There is no hiding the joy of a couple in love. They can bring a smile to the face of even the most fervent, ardent pessimist. They bring joy to everyone who sees them, everywhere they go—and they leave a trail of love, joy, and upliftment in their wake.

Lovers have the ability to look at everything with the soft eyes of open acceptance. Everything is so much more beautiful. Every moment can be a moment of lovemaking—the way we look at things, the way we touch things, the way we sense things, the way we do anything. There is no better time of life at all, except, perhaps, becoming a parent; that's another kind of love and another kind of adventure, and I still was not sure if I was going to experience that love and adventure in this lifetime, despite the less-than-subtle messages from Alana.

Our days were filled with many, many special moments: The smiles. The skipping of a heartbeat when he opened the door, coming home to me, at the end of the day. The merriment. The spontaneous laughs. The dimples slowly making their appearance as that lazy, rakish smile stretched across his face, instantly bringing a smile to my face in return. Sometimes I felt my heart could not take in all the grandeur, all the magnificence, and then my heart would surprise me and grow even bigger to hold all the majesty. And then it would grow even bigger the next day.

I danced through these days in total bliss, with complete, ongoing, ever-increasing gratitude.

Usually.

Being with Yeshua took quite a toll on me from time to time, too. I was so used to having my own way and commanding relationships that when I met someone who matched me—spiritually, intellectually, even stubbornly—I found myself at a loss from time to time. It was excellent training for me in staying centered and focused on who I am while also celebrating him and his strengths and assets...as well as celebrating the two of us together, because while we were each a power to be reckoned with on our own, together we were practically a force of nature.

Our time together was like a bubble sometimes. We would pray, meditate, make love, lie in each other's arms for hours and hours. We would live in such a sweet, high place that re-entering the regular world was like a star crashing to Earth. It was a shock to the system to rejoin society, where the primary emphasis was on food and money and grabbing and rushing from here to there and back again, when we had been living on light and being so generous with our love and needing to only be right where we were, right then.

And sometimes, because we were both so aware and we were teachers of this awareness, we would make each other absolutely crazy.

"That is not what I wanted," Yeshua said when that particular day brought him many people to talk to, heal, and teach. He had not commenced his full status as missionary, teacher, and healer yet, but was working up to being with more and more people.

"Well, obviously it is what you wanted," I said. "Otherwise you would not have created it."

"I cannot take that much at one time." He sighed. "Well, clearly I was not clear about what I wanted. The results always speak for themselves."

"That or the Beloved thinks you are ready, even if you don't." He groaned and pulled the bedcovers over his head. Yes, he was definitely quite human.

Sometimes even my sacred meditation could be a test for me, and having someone enunciate my imperfections in those moments was not high on my list of desires. One morning I found myself growing irritated with the sounds of the groundskeepers as they started their workday—right outside our quarters.

"What a wonderful meditation you are having," Yeshua chuckled.

"What makes you say that?"

"You're scowling. Your face is a grimace."

I found myself growing more irritated at him than at the groundskeepers. Then I smiled at my own silly nonsense. How effective could my meditation be, then, if I was sitting in a place of such irritation? Over nothing! And it certainly was not the groundskeeper's fault!

"That is better."

"Oh, hush." I hated it when he was right. Well, no, I did not, but you know what I mean.

It is very easy to be magnanimous, gracious,

benevolent, serene, noble, and peaceful when we are walking solo. We only have ourselves to answer to, our own plans to follow...and no one right in our space inconveniently reflecting ourselves back to ourselves— especially those times when we are being a lot less than we can be. How very annoying! Relationships with our true love, even those on the very highest levels, also often bring out our insecurities, our immaturities, our hidden faults...in short, anything and everything within us that still needs to be brought to light and dispelled. Oh, the joy.

But I got him back. All right, that is not a thought from the higher realms of my being. How's this: I had an opportunity to help him in one of his meditations, too, at one point. (And I loved it!) I watched him time after time as he held his hands over each chakra, starting with the root, then to the second chakra, and on up.

Now I know I do not have to explain to this spiritually advanced audience what chakras are, but in case one person reading or hearing this does not know, chakras are whirling vortexes of energy in certain places on the body. Clearing them regularly can allow us to function more optimally. The first of the seven main ones is the root chakra, in the groin area—this is the foundation of life, protection, and security; the second is just over the pelvic bone and the reproductive organs—this is the area of regenerative creativity; the third is just over the navel—this is the will and power seat; the fourth is over the heart—this is the place of love as well as where Heaven and Earth meet in loving connection within each one of us; the fifth is over the throat—this is the voice: expressive creativity; the sixth is over the third eye, just above the point between the eyebrows—this is our entry into the intuitive, perceptive, and mystical realms; the seventh is at the crown—the place where the Heavenly spiritual realms enter the body and where we are connected to the whole cosmos. There is an eighth chakra about a foot over the head, and many more going far above us, plus there are chakras in the feet, hands, and other places.

So Yeshua would start at the root and go up to his crown, one chakra at a time, clearing, day after day.

"Why do you always go in that direction?" I asked him one day.

"I'm taking my energy up to God," he answered.

"God's at both ends," I stated. He looked at me, struck for just a moment, and then laughed as he realized the truth of that statement. "As well as everywhere in between, too," I added.

"Well......" Not knowing how to respond and being at a loss for words was a rare occasion for him.

"And why not bring the Heavens into the body, too?" I demanded. "It's just as important." Only a woman firmly planted in her body could say this.

The next day he reversed direction.

Often our meditations were more physically and spiritually powerful than our lovemaking. Before a meditation sometimes he would caress my face ever so softly, so gently with the tips of his fingers. He gently rubbed the top of my head, and I wanted to merge and become one with the ground, like rain arriving on the scorched Earth. Then in the next moment I wanted to merge and become one with the sky, like that rain returning to where it came from. He rubbed my third eye, and a myriad of colors raced across my inner eye. I did the same for him and the effect was similar, I could sense.

At times, after hours in the silence, a vortex formed over us—a place of dazzling brilliance. The air sparkled and the usually unseen beings danced in ecstasy, elated that these two people had risen high enough to witness them.

☼

Speaking of some of my less-than-holy moments (as I just did with my admission of a less-than-higher-realm reaction to helping him with his meditation), there were times that I wanted to throw things at him, I was so angry. Being with my beloved and still experiencing these wild emotions made me better understand crimes of passion. I understand how someone can kill someone because here I was, a vastly awake human being compared to most, and I still had moments of extreme anger. Fortunately they would only last about two or three seconds at most, because I would quickly bring myself back.

But at some level we also sensed our time together was only for a short while. Knowing that gave us permission to let our love soar.

You heard us use the term counterparts in our wedding ceremony vows. There are spouses, there are partners, there are soul mates, there are twin flames. And then there are counterparts. Yeshua and I were counterparts. There have been only a few true counterpart matches, ever.

☼

Even with counterparts, not every day can be a beautiful, bliss-filled drop of paradise, however.

"Darling?" I called into our room upon my arrival home from the marketplace one afternoon.

"Nghhhhhh."

That was not exactly the response I had been looking forward to. "What is it, my darling? Are you alright?"

"Nnnnngggghhhhhhhhhh."

Have you ever had one of those conversations with your beloved partner? Well, I did, too. It took all my powers of will to not engage with him in moments like these. I put the food items and parcels away and went off to find someone else to talk with. Even the animals out grazing in the fields on the outskirts of the city would have been better company than Yeshua at these moments. Far better.

☼

And, yes, because our nearest and dearest relationships are always our nearest and dearest reflections of ourselves...

I came home one night to find Yeshua comfortably sprawled out on the cushions—far too comfortably for the amount of running around I had just done for both of us. I dropped all of my parcels and started banging pottery around.

"Was it something I said?"

"Oh, just let me be!" I banged around some more. He continued his sprawl, which just angered me all the more. "You wouldn't BELIEVE what I went through today. Oh, I can't believe how thick-headed some people are. Are you listening?"

Yeshua nodded, completely unsuccessful in his attempt to suppress a grin—which didn't help my mood any. I went upstairs to the bedroom. He didn't immediately follow me, which made things all the worse.

He finally came up about an hour later. I was in the bed but far from sleeping.

"And then they had the nerve to tell me it was my problem! The nerve!"

"Who?"

"And then you know what happened?"

"Mary?"

"Oh, just let me be!"

"Alright." He paused for a moment. "Isn't that what I've done for the last hour?"

I groaned and pulled the bedcovers up over my head.

"Despite your attempts to draw me in, I don't suppose you want any kind of response from me, really, do you?"

"No!" I stayed in the bad-mood-protecting-safety of the land under the bedcovers for a moment. "Because I know you'd be right, and I'm not in the mood for you to be right at this moment."

"It's not that you're wrong. But you also are in a mood to be in your mood."

"So let me!"

"I have been!"

That finally broke the mood and I burst out laughing. We laughed and laughed until he quieted my laughs with kisses. I'm sure no one out there can relate to this scene at all.

☼

My beloved had bouts of melancholy from time to time. No amount of understanding his work, of seeing the bigger view, could dissuade these periods. And no amount of words from me would help. I probably had moments like this, too, but I didn't notice my moments as much as his because mine did not necessarily bother me as much as his did. The only thing that helped was the passage of time. Plus, it seemed like after the times he would retreat into the recesses of the sadness, he would emerge with greater intention, greater wisdom, greater light.

So I usually left him alone to do his own returning, and he usually did the same for me when it was needed. Plus, our reunion always made the time apart worth it.

☼

As you already know, Yeshua and his parents lived in Egypt for many years, where much of my education and training came from, and we had many long discussions, sharing the different things that we knew. The people of ancient Egypt had learned many esoteric sciences. They created elixirs to prolong life, sometimes potions made of gold, sometimes potions made of the bloody discharge of women...if you think about it and realize that that physical material is designed to create and sustain life, then that idea would certainly make sense—although it certainly was not something I wanted to imbibe. We discussed at length the learnings from our own land and people. He also shared the teachings and ways of the East, with which I was far less familiar.

"There was a man who lived in the eastern land about, oh, perhaps five centuries ago," Yeshua told me once, "and he taught many things, especially the ways of the spirit. He was a prince and gave up the things of his world to seek truth, to be free. He was opened, and he saw, and he taught what he saw to others." Yeshua told me much of what the Buddha taught, and these were incorporated into the lessons and parables that Yeshua shared with the people. "He said that we are all Gods, which of course is something that I have always believed, despite what we are told."

"Yes. And while it's not new information to us, it certainly would be to the people of this land."

"Yes."

"Some might find it threatening."

"Yes." The tremor started but I did not want to go there with it yet. There would be plenty of time for that later.

"They also have a concept they call karma. They believe that everything someone does either hurts or rewards them later, whether in this life or in lives coming after this."

"Well, you and I believe that, too—with the idea of cause and effect."

"But we believe that we are our own source of the cause and effect."

"Yes, of course. Then this notion of karma, of causation—anything regarding it can be healed in an instant. It need not take lifetimes, or any time at all, really."

"Yes, you're right," Yeshua said slowly. "Yes, I guess that would be true."

Yeshua taught me some chants—salutes to the Divine—that he learned on his travels to the lands to the east. He also taught me some mudras—special positions for the hands. As we chanted together in meditation position with our hands held in mudras, such as the tip of the index finger pressed to the tip of the thumb, palms facing up, my hands started to tingle and burn. In those moments I felt like I could do anything or heal anyone, even more than from any spiritual practices I had already learned.

My primary physical attribute for that life was my hands, which often seemed to have a life of their own. Have you ever had one of those conversations where you decide if you absolutely had to give up seeing or hearing, which one would it be? People who adore music and sound would say they would more likely sacrifice their eyesight. People who thrill to the visual would say definitely they would give up their hearing.

Well, we had those conversations way back then, too. If I had to give up a sense, however, it would be anything but touch. In addition to feeling, I could hear things, even see things in my touch—far more than most. My fingers and hands could sense conditions in others that the eyes and ears could never pick up. Even the slightest touch on my body would send me to the realms of ecstasy. Touching another in healing or pleasure was my greatest joy.

☼

The idea of anyone going for days, weeks, months, years without touch is beyond baffling to me. I would recommend heartily that they pay someone. There's no need to go without touch.

☼

I was thinking along the lines of paying for a great massage. Is that not what were you thinking as well?

☼

The most surprising thing about him was that he was not what anyone would envision as a typical public figure. He was unassuming in his demeanor even while he held himself erect and strode purposefully—not in an arrogant way at all, but as someone who was humble yet knew he was a child of Eternity. He was not very big in stature either. The strong fishermen and carpenters and farmers who started to keep to his side dwarfed him, although he was still much, much bigger than I was. The difference with him was that he could speak the language of his audience, no matter who his audience was. And this made him seem much larger than he really was.

Given his preferences, he probably would have kept to himself and led a very quiet life, far away from the throngs of people who followed him. But he had a special calling. He had made an agreement before he came in to this world, and his entire purpose was to actualize that agreement—as has each and every one of us and as is the purpose of each and every one of us. His audience never became aware of his status as a somewhat reluctant teacher.

I'm not sure if you want to know this or not, but he had some bad habits. But then so did I. And so do you. He snored...and not just a gentle zzzzzzzzzzzz—he was like a lion roaring to protect its family. Sometimes I found it hard to fall asleep again once I was awakened by his fierce growling, and I was thankful to my years of meditation practice that I could spend the late night and early morning hours fruitfully. Then I would catch up later in the day, as soon as I was able, with a nap. Apparently, as he let me know, I snored from time to time, too, but not in quite the same fashion.

He had a couple other bad habits, but I will leave those to your imagination. I certainly would not want him to divulge mine either...not that he ever would.

One thing he did not seem to experience, ever, was bad dreams. Most men I spent the night with seemed to clash with marauding invaders or relive vicious past lives in their dreamtime. They would yell out and thrash about at times. I know dreams can be the mind's form of housekeeping, so Yeshua obviously already had a very clean house from his meditation and high state of awareness...not that I needed to spend nighttimes with him to find that out—one look at him would convey to anyone the high altitude of his life.

If he ever encountered a problem, he would not act on it until he had brought it to extensive prayer and meditation.

"I do not take one step toward resolving anything," he told me, "until the issue and I are completely filled by and surrounded with the presence of God."

This was good for me to hear, because while I was much better than most in my time, I would too often rush into the urgency of a situation and attempt to solve it as quickly as possible. And I spent most of my life in some form of prayer and meditation or another... and it still did not work as well as with Yeshua's way; the urgency often passed as he steeped and instilled himself in God, making whatever the issue was far more easily resolvable.

☼

A young apprentice came to my quarters one evening, her heart full of sorrow—something about some boy. Oh, if I had a shekel for every time a young priestess came to me with something about some boy, I would have been richer than Caesar. We trained our girls to realize that they were going to be far and above the level of understanding of most of the people of our city and country, perhaps the world, let alone boys their age. They could realize that they were above their families and most other people in realization of Truth, but when it came to boys, sometimes they would have a block. Not all of our girls were going to be trained in the art of lovemaking, and these were the ones who wanted to mingle with the boys their age. The girls who were primed in the sexual arts had no desire to mingle with boys nor deal with boy-crazy shenanigans.

"Mary, what can I do?" She did not seem to care that Yeshua was in the sitting room, too.

"My dear one, I do not suppose you'd want to hear my suggestion to forget all about him and move on?"

"No."

They never did. "Then be loving. If you want love, then be loving."

She wrinkled her face.

"That's how you get anything you want—give it! Be it! If you want love, give love, be love. If you want riches, then give money, be prosperous in your mind already. If you want more friends, then be a friend. If you want peace among your loved ones, then be peaceful. If you want to be forgiven, then forgive."

"What about beauty?" Oh, give them the prime pearls of the universe and they still want the basic Ten Commandments on how to get a boy to notice them.

"Then let your thoughts and words be beautiful. Speak beautiful words and ideas. Let your eyes shine— that is how anyone is beautiful."

"That's easy for you to say. You're already so very beautiful."

"Well, I pray, I meditate, I open to the Divine that is everywhere, I love, I let my light shine. That's all you need to be beautiful."

She, who was already a particularly beautiful girl, looked down.

"My little love," I said, "just be the love you are looking for. Then not only will you not need his love, but you will also have everything you need. Your deep love will reach out and only a deep love will answer. You will attract a love that is worthy of you, which could be him or someone even more on your level if he is not the one for you."

She looked at Yeshua, who had been smiling at our conversation. He nodded to her in affirmation of my words, trying unsuccessfully to look very serious.

"Thank you," she sighed. She bowed, hands in prayer position to forehead, and left the room.

"They would throw the entire world away for one

boy," I muttered.

"Is that not what you did?" He laughed at the look of surprise and then the smile that slowly spread across my face.

"Of course I did, and who could blame me?" I crawled onto the cushions and into his waiting arms. "I already had the entire world, the entire universe," I sighed. The wonder of the miracle that was my life overtook me. He gently brushed away the tear that was slipping down my cheek. "And then when you came back, it all just became even more brilliant than it already was. I did not think that was even possible."

"Yes. I know exactly of what you speak."

I brushed away the tear that was slipping down his cheek, too.

☼

Oh, my beloved Yeshua. Oh, my beloved. Oh, my Yeshua. The greatest love in our lives is here to show us how God loves us. I'd been with so many, yes, but I was saving my heart for him. And now he was with me. He was home. I was home.

From time to time my heart would quiver with the tremor—a momentary passing of fear. My greatest fear was that he would leave his body and leave this world, leaving me behind. Sometimes in moments of clarity I could sense that time was not very far off, and I could hold that knowledge in the high place, where it belonged. But other times I could not hold it in the higher place, and my heart ached.

"Mary, hush," I'd try to convince myself. "You know no one goes anywhere, even when they cross to the other side."

It sometimes worked. The only thing that really quelled the fear was the knowing that when it was time

to lay my body down, we would then be together for
eternity.

☼

No, I could not imagine a love greater than ours.
Perhaps there was one, sometime, somewhere, but that
was inconceivable to me.

☼

Such a profound love for another cannot come
without a profound love for ourselves. You are there, of
course. Well, all right, you are there in your higher
moments—I know you are. And in the moments that
are not so high, we all can lift ourselves up to the level
of how the universe views us and observe ourselves
from that level. The love is...well, there are just not
enough superlatives to describe that love. Magnificent.
All-encompassing.    All-powerful.    Omniscient.
Omnipresent. Glorious. Everywhere. Isn't it so
interesting that all the superlatives that can be used to
describe the All can also be used to describe love? That
is the love we can bestow on ourselves: the love of the
All.

We have been told for millennia to love our neighbor
as ourselves. But, my goodness, what about the people
who hate themselves? Oh, the poor neighbor! And if we
look around us, we see many people despising themselves and we see the results of this self-hatred. These
are the people inflicting pain and suffering on others.
They do not love themselves...how else could they reap
such destruction?

Oh, the divergent capacities of the human heart...
to love someone, a child or a spouse, so completely, so
selflessly, that we would lay our lives down for him or

her...or to devise cruel ways of imprisoning, torturing, and killing a brother or a sister...or to lead people to a new way of thinking and being...or to control people and manipulate them for one's own power. In some areas someone would kill us over water...food...the color of our skin...control...the way we think...the way we pray...the way we heal...the way we love and make love or for the person we choose to love and make love to. To think that some people have died, at the hands of others who do not understand, because of who and how they chose to love!

As you know by now, ultimately there is no such thing as death anyway. Yeshua's life was all about teaching that...but, well, more about that later.

If there was one thing I could add to life on Earth, it would be that each person is taught and learns the sacred sanctity of life, in themselves and in all others. To *love*, really love, with all their heart. Thankfully this is coming. This is where life is headed.

In our moments of trial and tribulation we can ask, What would Yeshua do? What would Mary do? What would (the person who has most beneficially influenced you) do? Most important, what would Love do? Then, what would I do?

And if no answer makes itself readily known, ask yourself what would I do if I already knew what to do?

☼

Love has a very special name...and, among its many, many special names, one of its most wonderful names is whatever you call yourself.

# CHAPTER 6

Yeshua had a smile that could melt hearts, along with a deep, infectious belly laugh that could bring a smile to the face of even the most cynical, hardened, grimacing grouch. Laughing was considered a great extravagance by most of the people most of the time in those days, so his bright light, merry ways, and loud, booming laugh made him quite a spectacle.

Tears are a sign of an opened heart, and so is laughter. Sometimes I think that enabling people to laugh is one of the greatest gifts anyone can give to another. Laughing and merriment and joy raise our vibration, and a raised vibration lifts up everyone around us—even in other dimensions and other galaxies...but that's another book.

"Do you know you light up a whole room just by showing up in the doorway?" he once asked me.

His words made me laugh because of course at that very moment I was thinking the exact same thing about him.

Little children flocked to him, animals stayed by his side, even old women would seek his company because he would flirt, ever so subtly, with them—reminding them of what they might have felt years earlier...or what they could have felt years earlier, but probably did not, as the case more likely was. Old men would seek his counsel and even teenagers would listen to him. One afternoon I laughed at him as he was balancing a toddler on his knee while holding a baby in his other arm while a dog nuzzled his hand that was balancing the toddler for a pat while an old woman giggled at a look he sent in her direction while debating with an older man while even a donkey came along wanting to sit down beside him.

And of course he said they were all there because of me, while I was balancing another toddler, holding another baby, gently flirting with an old man. But I did not see any donkeys wanting to sit down beside me.

☼

When Yeshua was a teenager, his parents found him in a temple talking to the priests and scribes. That was true; what the bible says he said to his parents was not exactly true.

"I am about my Mother Father God's business," was his reply to their stern interrogation, once they recovered from the fear that he was lost. This was the dedication of his life, from the very moment he decided to incarnate. Once he had traveled and learned much, once he returned and married me, once he had some exposure to the people of Israel, he felt ready to start talking to and healing more and more. And more. And more. His ability to teach and be heard as well as to heal was becoming well known throughout the land.

Perhaps the writers of old could not guess how else someone could work masterfully with their hands? Ah, he must have been a carpenter! Although if he was supposed to be the Son of God and could manifest wine, loaves, and fishes, why would he have had to be a carpenter? Or even work at all?

Yes, I'm digressing...you know me well by now... back to my story. The Twelve actually approached him at different points over the following year. You already know their names—the writers did get those right. They were fishermen, shepherds, woodworkers, and builders. Yeshua's brother, James, was among them. They had little education and no formal training in religion or anything other than their field of work, but Yeshua recognized an opening in them. Each one of them initiated the contact with him, as did many others, but he invited this particular dozen to come back time and again.

We started gathering together—not just Yeshua and me with the Twelve; sometimes their wives (yes, wives!), children (yes, a few had children), brothers, sisters, cousins, neighbors would join us at the urging of Simon or Peter or the others, but those other invitees seldom returned. The discussions often continued all through the night until the next day's light. We would gather at various homes or more often on the temple grounds, sometimes in the larger meeting halls or classrooms, or sometimes squeezing into our own sitting room if the size of the gathering allowed it.

"What I do, you can do," Yeshua insisted.

"No, Teacher," would be their reply. "You have a special gift."

"A gift that was given to each one of us."

"You have not seen us healing any lepers of their disease!"

"How many of you have tried?" The Twelve shrugged and looked around the room at anyone except Yeshua. "Why would a creator create some of us with a great gift and not the others? True, some of you have a gift for building a home, and I could not do that. Some of you have a gift for keeping your flocks together, and I would have a hard time doing that. Others are talented with procuring merchandise and creating a thriving business where others would give up. But we all can speak words of truth and heal, if we would but recognize and cultivate these talents."

"How do we start?"

"*Not that which goeth into the mouth defileth a man; but that which cometh out of the mouth, this defileth a man*."

While they stared at him with blank expressions, he turned to me.

"Speak words of love, truth, and healing," I said to them. "Let nothing else leave your lips; indeed, let nothing else fill your thoughts. What you give out is far more important than anything you take in. A destructive thought can be as harmful as a destructive action. Remember this always and live this way. Let Truth fill your being to overflowing. Then you are of service to teach and heal. Easily."

Some of the Twelve took to our words readily; for others it took weeks, months for our words to be absorbed and assimilated, let alone embodied. One evening Peter watched me speak with some of my students who had approached our meeting room with a question for me regarding a difficult lesson I taught earlier that day. Yeshua was talking quietly with a few of the others, and after the students left Peter took the opportunity to speak with me.

"He's telling us to go forth and heal," Peter said. "But how does he do it, really?"

"He doesn't, really," I answered. "He is a clear channel for the healing. But by their answer, his patients actually do most of the work."

"Then how does he heal the sick?

"It is in his question, '*Wilt thou be made whole*?' He does not do anything—he just makes the possibility available, and they do their own miraculous healing. By their answer of yes, the work is done."

These were men who, while they were somewhat advanced, were also a product of their time. They were not as far along as Yeshua, and so hearing answers from me—a woman, oh my goodness—that they did not already know themselves was very hard for them. Listening to me became easier with time, though;

proximity can be everything, sometimes. And I wasn't always polite. When Yeshua brought one, two, three people "back from the dead," I practically wanted to hit them over the head (lovingly, of course) at their obstinate insistence that truly a miracle happened.

"He did not raise them from the dead!" I nearly yelled at them. "They were in the place between worlds, and they had not yet decided to fully leave this one yet. Yeshua merely called them back. And they would not have come back if they had not wanted to, if the call from the other side was greater for them."

Sometimes I think it is far easier to retell the stories of old to you—you who have had a certain version of things imbedded in your psyche, if not your DNA, too, as well as ingrained in the very fabric of society for over two thousand years—than it was to tell them that what they think happened did not.

One night Judas approached Mark on the walk home from Peter's lodging room after a long discussion over dinner on the God within and feeling more like God, not realizing that Yeshua and I were right behind them.

"And just how exactly are we to feel more like God?" he asked.

The two men then noticed us behind them. Mark did not answer. The group of us continued walking in silence. We reached Mark's temporary home, which he shared with some of the others while they were staying in Jerusalem. Judas stopped with him while Yeshua and I continued into the night.

"By acting more Godlike," I called back. The darkness enveloped my words, but I knew they heard me, especially Judas.

☼

My students asked me that all the time, and it was one of my favorite questions to answer. "If everything's God, and if we're God, since we're part of everything, how can we actually *feel* more like God?"

"By acting more like God," I would answer. "How do you think a person fully aware of their God/Goddess self would act? Would they be lazy? Would they be stingy? Would they be greedy? Or would they give as much of their time and talent and love as they could, with little thought of a reward? Would not the joy of their work and service, as well as the benefit to the people they touch, be the reward?"

I'd let that float around their awareness for a few moments and then continue. "A person living in their true nature of God would never do something unkind, unfair, unlawful, miserly—not because of punishment, retribution, or even causation, but because being fair, kind, law-abiding, and generous are the ways to be. For their own reward. And because they could not possibly be any other way."

Once their faces registered that they understood, I continued yet again. "Would people who were living in their true Godself lie? Would they try to deceive or cheat someone? Would they manipulate something for their benefit? Would they steal? I'm not even talking about stealing physical things, although that is bad enough. But even beyond that, on the subtler levels, would a person coming from their Godself try to steal someone's joy? Have you ever begrudged a friend's good fortune or success...or boyfriend? If you begrudge a sister her special relationship, that just waylays your own special relationship. If you begrudge a sister her good fortune, that just waylays your own good fortune."

Several girls always shifted uncomfortably at that.

"If you wish someone ill will, even for just a fraction of a second, you are actively bringing that into your own life." Even more uncomfortable shifting passed through the room like a wave.

I'd overheard many conversations where a student was begrudging a sister something wonderful that had come her way. And then in the same conversation the same girl would be wondering why her own wonderful something or other was not readily forthcoming.

"Yes, acting more Godlike and thus being more Godlike commands vigilance and staying on the higher path. It is not the easier way at first, but it does become easier and easier as you become more and more and more used to it."

When they were out of their temporary pangs of worry and back into receptive mode, I'd continue.

"And once you've mastered the life-here-on-Earth realms, it goes into the inner realms. Would people living in the God/Goddess self steal someone else's energy? Would they try to thrive on someone else's light? Would they let someone try to take their own joy or energy or light? Would they withhold their heart and energy and love because they'd rather be stubborn and unyielding? Or would they do none of these things and share their entire being and spirit as God would share them? Would they not be aware of the all-giving, all-providing nature of All That Is and act graciously and willingly share their resources, ideas, opportunities, talents, and even their good thoughts, energy, light, and love?"

My students were always quiet for a long time after that question, pondering the times they have acted Godlike and the times they could have acted in a way far more becoming and suited to the higher life to which they had been called.

"And," I said in conclusion, "the most Godlike thing of all: do good for everyone, all the time, as well as you can...and be quiet about it."

☼

I often considered that I had an easier time teaching
my students these rather revolutionary—for the time—
laws of life than Yeshua had with the Twelve, possibly
because they were so much younger and had not had
the fears of the time heaped upon them day after day,
year after year, as long as the Twelve had. But Yeshua
had a very, very special gift. His primary teaching was
unconditional love, and he expressed this in every
word, every motion. People were drawn to him because
few others were like him. He offered a direct path to the
Divine. And it did not hurt that he was a handsome,
loving, laughing, confident wayshower.

God/Goddess is the power behind everything, everywhere, including within us. Yet sometimes we yearn for
a more personal connection with the great vastness out
there—and even with what can sometimes seem like
the great vastness in there, inside ourselves. So we
need...a personality, perhaps. A face. A smile. That is
probably why Yeshua became so popular in his time
and down through the ages. He is a warm, soft, smiling
face of God. But so are our beloveds. So are our
mothers. So are our babies. So are our animal
companions. So are angels. These are all a personal
connection to Mother Father God. God wraps Its arms
around us in innumerable forms, every minute of every
day, if we would but notice. God speaks to us through
the voices of our friends and families, through the song
of the bird, and through the winds rustling the tall
grasses. Yeshua told us this, often, but sometimes
people can become more captivated with the messenger
than with the message they bring.

Yeshua was a warm, soft, smiling face of God in a
time when people needed a warm, soft, smiling face as

their connection to the Infinite, then and even now, still. He could speak in terms that people understood. He could heal...as we all can heal; some of us just do not know that yet. He tried to pass these teachings on to everyone, but especially to the Twelve, so they could carry on his teachings—after all, the more teachers, the more the teachings could be heard and received.

But it was far from easy. At times Yeshua would get extremely frustrated with them.

"They cannot be faulted," I said. "They just do not know. But they are learning quickly, as you teach them."

"And as you teach them. Thankfully you are here, too, and I'm not doing this all on my own." He fiddled with the food on the supper plate lovingly delivered by Rachel. "It is as if they are under a spell."

"As if? It is not as if...they *are* under a spell, as almost everyone is. But you can talk to them as others cannot."

He set the plate aside and stared out the window.

"My darling," I said, "you are creating something for them that probably would not have otherwise existed. And when they understand, your words will extend much farther than they otherwise would have, through them. But you must be patient with them. They are not like you."

"But they are."

"True. But they do not realize that yet."

And, yes, that is what I meant way back toward the beginning of this story—do you remember? I said that he and I were just like you, only more so. I'm sure you understand what I meant by that by now.

☼

Judas became another soul brother to me. He was

my preferred of the Twelve, as he had an air of innocence about him and was the most open to learning. You can be sure I will be telling you much more about him later. He also was less a product of his time than the other men, for some reason; he was closer to Yeshua in that regard. He respected my status as a teacher more than the others, and he frequently approached me for long, private discussions.

"He is special," Judas said to me one night as he was about to leave our sitting room. The others were still in a heated discussion.

"As are you. Yes, you are," I said, responding to his look of skepticism. "No one is extra special and yet we all are incredibly special," I replied. "There is something that each one of us brings to life here in this realm, something that no one else could give or do. Our purpose for being here."

"Perhaps even I will do something of great significance," he said with a hint of awe at the thought that he possibly could.

"I am sure you will."

☼

"Oh, God, please!" James was struggling with the malady faced by one of the people he was trying to heal.

"James," Yeshua said to him later that day, "you never have to say, 'God, please!' The one you have to say, 'Please' to, always, is yourself. God has already said, 'Yes,' always. Our job is just to say, 'Thank you.'"

"Yes." James thought for a moment. "But is it not the sick one's desire for the healing that will do it?"

"Yes, but the clearer you are, the greater the healing that can occur. Your patient can catch hold of your power if you are a clear transmission of love and light. And then he or she can say a clear, 'Yes.' For anything you desire, the task is not to persuade a petulant, withholding God; the task is to open the doorway within yourself. God is never withholding. All has already been given. It is your task to receive it."

☼

So many people! The crowd pressed in on us. Word was spreading of Yeshua's healings, and they came to him by the hundreds, then by the thousands.

It was one of my rare local ventures with him. I saw a very sick woman, who was hemorrhaging. She touched the hem of his garment. Despite the throngs of people jostling him, Yeshua felt her touch and he turned to her.

He looked deep into her eyes. "Your faith has made you well."

Tears slipped down her face as she nodded to him.

☼

"You are a clear vessel for the light of the Divine to come through you," Yeshua told them that night. "That's your only job. Be clear. And know the truth of perfection for the person you are working with."

All twelve of them stammered and sputtered for a moment or two, not quite knowing how to ask their questions.

"Your job is to know for them what God knows about you," I said to them. "You are perfect. You are so loved. You are the son of God. The woman Yeshua helped bring to wholeness today is the daughter of God, and all he really did was help her remember that."

We let them sit in silence for a long while, letting our words sink in.

It slowly started to make sense to them. Each day seemed to solidify the resolve in the heart of each of the disciples, and their further opening brought up more and more questions, which Yeshua was only too happy to answer.

"Teacher, why do we see so much suffering?"

"Yes, teacher, why? If God is so loving and just, why would there be such disparity among us? Some are sick; some are not. Some are wealthy; some struggle even to find a morsel to eat."

Yeshua's answers, sometimes with my assistance, and the ensuing discussions would continue for hours and hours.

Ah, yes, suffering is such an interesting discussion. We see people with life-threatening illnesses—dying years before what we would consider to be their time, newborns with grave deformities, rape and torture, murder, people imprisoned unjustly, slavery, starvation, young lives snuffed out through senseless wars, and even the attempt to wipe out races or ethnicities of our species...and we ask how can this possibly be? Why is this so? I say again that every single life is eternal, part of the whole that was never born and can never die, but is always present. We do not know what choices individual souls and soul groups have made before they incarnated. But the knowledge, wisdom, power, and love of All resides in each one of us. There are no mistakes. There might be grave tragedies and travesties—situations we would view as unfair—but we do not always have access to the bigger picture, which would hold the reason for the situation at the highest level.

And then many people go through a personal suffering of their own creation: a preoccupation with the negative. Too much eating or drinking or sexing or...anything we do with the sole intent and objective of taking ourselves out of ourselves. It is a way to numb the senses. It is a way to feel more powerful, better about ourselves...perhaps a way to get that feeling of being one with the beloved, as best we can. But there are much, much better ways to attain that feeling.

But back to what we would term seemingly random, unjust suffering....The soul might have developed whatever tragedy or travesty we are facing to do any one of a myriad of favors for us. Such as....

Take us on a closer walk with the Divine.

Strengthen our spirits.

Crack open our hearts.

Bring us humility.

Then make us even more humble.

Bend our knees in faith.

Temper the soul.

Fortify us.

Prepare us.

Awaken us.

Courage is not being without fear; courage is being in fear and moving forward in the direction the heart is guiding us anyway. If we are never in situations requiring courage, graciousness, and indomitable spirit, how would we know what we are made of? It would be easy to walk through a rose garden all of our lives...the test comes in the drought when the beautiful garden withers away, or when the roses get trampled, and we can embrace a higher resolve and make it even more beautiful than it was before.

Whatever the situation, the most important thing is not the situation itself—it is the reaction to the situation. One kind of response to being imprisoned unjustly can make us incredibly gallant human beings. Or a certain response to the tragic death of a loved one can make us the person that others come to in their time of need. And one sort of response to a sickness can bring us closer to the God/Goddess within.

Yet even though we know that suffering can be a training or an opening, or whatever the soul is calling forth, all people deserve our loving compassion in their times of pain, no matter what their circumstances. As I just mentioned, the primary message that Yeshua emerged from the quiet of his years of solitude and meditations to teach was...unconditional love.

Love lives in and powers each and every atom in all of infinite space and time, in the whole of eternity, and certainly lives in and powers our lives. This love reaches out and attracts our definition of the domain of Heaven to us. If we want to live a new, better definition of that domain, all we have to do is increase the flow of love, starting with the flow to ourselves and then the flow out to others.

At this point in my life, I had not faced tremendous pain and tragedy...yet. Many people around me had left their physical bodies, of course, but I never viewed that as tragic—it was the next step in their ongoing adventures of forever. But my soul knew what was to come for me in this life, and I received my preliminary training elsewhere, and then I certainly received my extreme training as events unfolded.

There are some among us who seem not to have suffered at all, but have somewhat muddled through life, sometimes catastrophizing things, sometimes being fearful and insecure for no apparent legitimate reason... until a great tragedy comes along and wakes them from their little selves, and they emerge into a far more glorious version of what they once were. Have you ever noticed that some of the most powerful and spiritual people and great teachers are those who have suffered greatly? It is as though their own souls have to go through a trial and a tempering before they can truly pass on wisdom to others. And then are they not the ones who can laugh the hardest and longest and most frequently?

Perhaps we are coming to a time where our teachers do not have to suffer so much any more. But in the meantime, they are the ones who can truly teach, they are the ones people can hear, they are the chosen ones for that particular calling—that of teaching and healing on the larger scale.

☼

We are all the chosen ones for our own particular calling.

And we are all called.

And perhaps we are being called to the highest path of all: to die with dignity, with the name of God, Life, Love, or however we want to call the Beloved, on our lips, forgiving the person who is taking life from us. It is a rare person who can perform that feat, but more than one has done it. I am not talking about martyrdom, I am talking about a God-centered acceptance. There is a vast difference and this acceptance is a glorious upliftment of us all.

☼

*Wilt thou be made whole?*

Yes.

And so it is.

By the allowance in the answer, the healing is done.

☼

One time a student was missing. We finally found

her hidden away in a storage area behind the cooking building. She had made a little nest for herself of blankets in amongst the gardening tools and cooking supplies. Her body raged with a fever, and I noticed a lump on the side of her neck.

"My darling, why have you hidden yourself away, where no one could be with you and help you?" I asked her.

She could barely talk, but one of her closest sisters spoke up for her. "You often tell us to be so strong, so independent, that we can do things ourselves and we don't need anyone else's help."

"But everyone needs help from time to time," I said. "Remembering that you can live without others' help constantly is what is most important. But no one is above the healing hand of another. Otherwise, what would we have each other for? There would only need to be one of us here."

"But there is only one of us here, at least that is what you always tell us," my star pupil stated.

"Correct, there is only one of us here. But in so many different, wonderful manifestations."

I put my hand over the lump and breathed into it.

"Every single day you tell us to be positive and we'll have all things added to us," the girl continued.

"So it's *my* fault that I'm sick," whispered the girl on the blankets. "I didn't think well enough."

"No, no," I said to her, "it is not your *fault*. It is your *gift*. It is your *power*. You took it on. You are the one in control of your life. You are the one who made the decision to have this, for whatever reason, whether you made that decision last week, last year, or last incarnation. It is not your fault. It is your right, it is your fortune, it is your lesson, it is your liberation from something we do not quite see right now, it is your initiation into something new that we also do not quite see yet, it is your piece of the Goddess expressing, it is your power that created this. This is not bad. There is no fault here at all; there is no blame. There must be only acceptance. And if you can claim responsibility for every manifestation in your life, then you are not a victim—you are the one in control of your life. And you can cocreate with the Goddess for anything to happen. Anything."

She dissolved the tumor in the next few days.

☼

Lessons do come from the harder route sometimes. Why would God let us suffer so much? Well, you would never help your child learn to walk by holding her hand constantly, would you? No, you'd let her fall...and fall...and fall...and pull herself up...and pull herself up...and pull herself up...many times...until she finally gets it. And get it she will.

☼

"Does someone experience the life they deserve, then?" my students would ask me frequently.

How could anyone say that someone who spends life as a slave has the life he or she deserves? Quid pro quo karma, say some; perhaps he or she enslaved someone in a past life. Oh, but then perhaps not. Perhaps God in Its infinite capacity to express and create has set it up for us to experience lives as both the master and the slave...and to experience the chains that bind them both. Perhaps the lesson is to be on both ends of the sword, and to die in one life as one has killed in another life. Those who live by the sword....As you sow....And perhaps the lesson is also to be on both sides of starvation. It is excruciating to be a starving person in a particular lifetime...and it is even worse to be someone who could have done something about rampant starvation yet did nothing.

☼

And everyone can do something.

# CHAPTER 7

There is a layer surrounding Earth that is made up of more than air. Some people think of the Earth as a living, breathing organism, which she is. And she also thinks. When innovative ideas and news want to be conveyed, they are carried in this thinking layer. We do not have to be telepathic; we only need to tune into this layer. Often many similar creations are completed, many identical ideas are birthed, many items are invented at the same time, because the creators, thinkers, and inventors have all picked up the idea from this esoteric covering. In fact, there are many stories starting to emerge about me these days; well, of course—it is my time to emerge.

And so even before Yeshua started speaking to the masses, without the assistance of near-instantaneous, speed-of-light global media, his reputation went before him. He started traveling all over Israel, speaking to people in temples, on the streets, in small villages, in large cities, on the hillsides. Many people greeted him as if they already knew him, and perhaps they did already know him. Certainly John was among those people.

We'd heard of the Baptist for several months and finally went to see him. John stood in the river as swarms of people waited in line along the banks to be dunked by him, none too gently, and then have a gentle stream of water poured over their crowns. He performed this act for several people, and then he stopped his work and looked around him at the crowd, certainly searching for someone in particular. When he finally spotted Yeshua standing higher up the hillside, somewhat apart from the throngs, John charged up the hill to him.

"You are the one we have been waiting for."

"No, I'm not—"

"Yes, you are he."

John pulled Yeshua down the hillside and into the river, pushed him down so that his shoulders were submerged, dunked his head, and then poured water over his crown. A bright light flashed over Yeshua's head, and at just that moment a white dove flew over them. Now I had seen the fire over people's heads many times, when they are connected to the Divine within and without. But this crowd obviously had not experienced such a sight before. A gasp went up, then a stunned silence, and then people started talking all at once.

"What was that?"

"Did you see that flash of light?"

"Did that dove just appear over his head?"

And so the exaggerations started.

☼

Have you ever noticed in the accounts of his story how often Yeshua was found staying or supping at someone else's house? In reality, unless he or we were on the road far from Jerusalem, nine nights out of ten we would sup at our own home. Most days we would load up several sacks with flatbread, olives, figs, and skins, some filled with water, some filled with wine, for our day-long sojourns through our city and on the outskirts, but we longed to return to the meals that Rachel loving prepared for us. Actually, I frequently had to remind Yeshua to eat. He consumed and lived on love, light, and air, but if he only did that he would become too thin and, these days especially, he needed more strength. Some people can live on very little, even on just air; but those people generally are not speaking to massive crowds. For that kind of mission, more food energy is required.

Sometimes he would not sleep for days but instead would devote his nights to prayer, meditation, long discussions, or healing. At some eventual point, however, he would need to sleep, and sleep he would— sometimes for several days at a time, to replenish his energy. This was very different from the way I lived. I could go without a meal here and there or without sleep for a night here and there; usually, however, I went to sleep and awoke at the same times every day and could be very testy if I was denied my rest. I also needed to eat full meals regularly. I was very much meant to be in my body in that lifetime, and my body would protest loudly if I tried to ignore it.

At times Yeshua and I would journey together, but far more often he would journey on his own or with the Twelve. Sometimes many weeks would go by without me seeing him, but often many a great tale about him would wend its way back to me long before he did.

"Did you hear I calmed the winds and the mighty seas?" he said upon one particular return.

"I did hear that! I also heard that you can walk on water. Are there any other great feats you've performed that I should know about?" I laughed with him. The now all-too-familiar quick tremor in my heart quelled the laughter. "That is how outrageous stories, even myths start," I said, too sharply perhaps. Yeshua looked at me in surprise at my harsh tone. "Something happens by circumstance; then, the very next thing you know, that person is known for pushing a huge rock up a mountain, or catching lightning in his teeth, or calming the winds and the seas. And those who jealously safeguard their own false power become afraid."

"Yes," he replied. "But sometimes that is what is supposed to be."

The tremor shook me again. But I knew he was right. And I knew both of us took this lifetime on willingly. Oh, why could not the part of everyone that knows the truth consistently and fully assure the part that insists on being fearful? But if we knew everything, if there was nothing to overcome, there would not be much purpose to our days on this Earth. If there was never anything unwell, would we fully comprehend and know what wellness is? If we were completely perfect all the time there would not be much point in the Earth walk.

☼

Who wrote the bible?

Well, who's writing this? A human being. Right—so who wrote the bible? A human being. All right, several human beings. All right, several dozen human beings over time. Emphasis on human. And time.

If folks told you they talked to God up on a mountain and God appeared to them as a burning bush, you would look at them funny. As well you should. If someone told you that his wife turned around and was turned into a pillar of salt, you would certainly look at him funny, too. As well you should. I mean, perhaps a burning bush on a mountaintop could happen, but a human being transformed into a pillar of salt certainly could not happen. So why were not the writers of the bible looked at funny? As well they should have been. And do not even get me started on that serpent!

If people today announced that they were writing the word of God, dictated directly from the mouth of God, chances are the authorities would have them locked up and put far, far away so they could not inflict great harm on society. Too bad the authorities of old did not do the same for the bible-writers of old.

The bible is made up. It is as much fact as are the stories about Zeus and Poseidon and Demeter and Persephone. Most of the bible is myth—and not even original, innovative myth but recycled myth at that, back from the days when humans were even more mystified by the world around them.

Is anything that I am writing about any crazier than a virgin birth, a burning bush, or a boatload of animals? I mean honestly—did Noah go all the way to the northern ice to gather up the polar bears and then all the way to the southern ice to gather up the penguins? How could anyone......? Well, anyway....

If that offends you, by all means do not continue reading this and go back to reading the bible...until the time comes that you can embrace an all-loving, all-peaceful God. If you still have need of the vengeful, patriarchal, capricious God of old, for whatever reason, then by all means stay with it. Or if your entire faith rests on Jesus Christ being the only Son of God, then go back to reading the bible...until the time comes that you can embrace your own divinity. If you still have need of the humanity-as-worm-in-the-dust scenario—for whatever reason—then by all means have at it. But Yeshua and I would, with all the love in our hearts, invite you to look at some higher places in which to place your faith and hence look at some much higher possibilities for your life...and hence a higher you.

I am sure the ancient Greeks and Romans were upset to find out that their very compelling gods and goddesses did not exist either. But they certainly got over it rather well.

So people have been killing each other for centuries over myths, over fairy tales. People have been taking possession of land based on promises by a God that never existed. People are still living as elitists.

Drop it!

We are all divine incarnations of eternal life.

It's just that some of us know it and some of us are coming to know it in time. And some will take even longer.

But the rising tide raises all boats.

☼

The gospels were written—yes, by human beings just like you—years and years after Yeshua lived. Some of the stories are somewhat true. I do not want to translate and rewrite all of Matthew, Mark, Luke, and John for you here, but I will give some highlights of our story from the perspective of someone who was actually there.

The bible—indeed, all of history—needs to be looked at askance. Chronicles were kept by the victors and written the way they wanted things to be remembered. You know how one message can get wildly misconstrued when it is repeated just once or twice. And you know how one story can be told in a particular way by an elder and in a completely different way by a teen-ager. Oftentimes you would not even think they were talking about the same event!

So, yes, what he said was a little different from what was said that he said. No...it was not a little different; it was *very, very* different. The words that the bible attributes to Yeshua (yes, the words in red) are sometimes harsh and unloving. Sometimes the words are anti-family, which is highly convenient for a Church that desires its priests to leave all of their money and property to the Church and not to their families—either their families of origin or the families they could have had. Sometimes the words seem misogynistic. And sometimes the words are sectarian and elitist. None of this is the way he talked—at all.

If you really want to know what he said, think of the most inclusive, loving words you can imagine. Remove everything even close to unkind. Remove anything even resembling gender bias. Remove harsh commands and admonishments. Remove all things that are against the family. Remove references to God as the Father or Him. Remove elitism, superiority, and separatism. Remove... most of it.

Perhaps the best thing to do with Yeshua's teachings as you have read them is to read them again and translate them into a sentence that uses gender-neutral terms; that emphasizes inclusivity, forgiveness, and compassion; that encourages spiritual seeking but not to the detriment of family and community...then you will come closer to what he was teaching and preaching. So instead of God the Father or Heavenly Father, he made reference to Mother Father God, or God/Goddess/All That Is, or the All, or Life. That very famous question, *"Who is my mother?"*—well, considering everything you now know about this beautiful, beloved man named Yeshua and how much he absolutely adored his mother, does that sound even remotely like something he would say? I did not think so. And as far as telling people to drop everything and just follow him—well, that just did not happen either.

The language and linguistic customs of my time gave words different meanings and nuances. So what might sound exclusive and elitist in modern languages was far from that in my language of old. When Yeshua told the multitudes what you currently hear as *"I am the way, the truth, and the life,"* what he was saying in our language was something like "Come with me, I can teach you, and you will know the path of truth and light." What you hear as *"No man cometh unto the Father, but by me,"* refers to his example of healing and uplifting the people of the time...more like "you can see the Beloved in the things that I do." And, of course, *"Thou shalt see greater things than these,"* in the fullness of time, he did say again and again.

So what you might hear today as a request to his students to drop everything and follow him was not a literal request at all. It was a metaphysical request to emotionally, mentally, and spiritually leave the things of their lives that no longer served them and to follow Yeshua's way as best they could—and not from where they were but from where they could be. And if that meant literally following him on the road, that was fine, too, but it certainly was not the only prerequisite to living the life he espoused.

He did say, *"Let the dead bury their dead"* but not to make a requirement that a grieving man leave his family in its time of need. Instead this would have been on the same level as let *"thine eye be single."* You know how newspapers go for the most captivating headlines these days, even to the point of employing scare tactics; well, that is probably what these writers were doing, too, at the behest of the Church.

Yeshua did not cast out devils. You are wise enough to know now that the devils they were referring to were split personalities, soul damage, and sometimes extreme psychotic breakdowns. It was an exceedingly hard time to be alive, and many people chose to live in an altered reality so they could better bear the brutality of the day. In some instances Yeshua's word was enough to bring them back to this side of reality.

You have heard something along the lines of "You who see me see Him who brought me." As you now know, Yeshua would not have said Him, he would have said, "That which brought me." *"That if two of you shall agree on earth as touching any thing that they shall ask, it shall by done for them of my Father which is in heaven."* Of course he would have said Mother Father God in Heaven, inside. He was gender neutral, always, when he referred to anything, especially our Creator. Not so was the case with those who chronicled the events of his life. And Heaven was not out there but here, up close, in this very moment of our lives, and in here, deep within each one of us.

He basically said, "Come with me. Walk the way of love, peace, joy, and plenty. Open your hearts. Pray, believing, and it shall be so."

No one else in that place and time had spoken like that. Roman governors were not known for emphasizing love in their speeches. Not many priests and scribes were extolling the virtues of cooperation in place of competition. In the dwellings, most parents' emphasis was on holding home and hearth and family together as best they could, not examining the intricacies of the spirit.

Now, granted, if I had been in charge of such a dour, negative, scared group of people in the midst of the major crossroads of several continents, people who thought absolutely nothing of taking something that did not belong to them or even taking a human life with nary a second thought, I might have invented a harsh and judgmental God, a Judgment Day, a fiery pit of Hell, and the lure of a far-off promised land, too. Maybe it did bring all the clashing tribes from different worlds more into line over the centuries than they would have been otherwise. But could they not have been even more in line if they had been taught to revere the sacredness of Life as it dwelt within them and their neighbors? Or how about something more basic—that if they steal something from someone else, they will have something stolen from them...the simple yet unavoidable law of cause and effect.

But perhaps it might have been too much for them. The people obviously wanted to be treated like mischievous, errant children, taken to task by their religion through the stern reprimands—much like a very strict father—of the priests...and ultimately judged by a very harsh, unloving God.

Yeshua's ideas, if taken at the level they truly were at, might very well have created anarchy, even more than they did—massive, widespread mayhem. So people's subjective hearing turned his words into verses that would fit into the times, and hence a patriarchal God, a little more.

Sometimes Yeshua would actually speak in those terms, to reach his audience, and would then slip in his new ideas in snippets, so as not to overwhelm them.

*"Take no thought for your life, what ye shall eat; or what ye shall drink, neither for the body, what ye shall put on."* And, yes, he talked of the lilies and the things sought by the nations. *"Fear not, little flock; for it is your Father's good pleasure to give you the Kingdom."* That particular crowd understood this, so he went on. "And of course, there is no Heaven out there, no Father out there. The domain of Heaven is within each one of us and is everywhere. Mother Father God lives within each one of us, is each one of us." That was certainly somewhat different from what has been attributed to Matthew, Mark, Luke, and John.

And then sometimes his words came down through the ages exactly as he said them: *"And all things, whatsoever ye shall ask in prayer believing, ye shall receive."* And *"Ask, and it shall be given you; seek, and ye shall find; knock, and it shall be opened unto you."*

Obviously there could not be any improvement or translation on clear, vivid, transparent truth. Nor could there be any marring of it, even by those with unscrupulous motives.

☼

He could be ornery, too, when he wanted to be. We both could...not with each other, so much, although as you know that certainly happened from time to time, but with others who thought our ideas and teachings were preposterous—frivolous, even—and tried to stop us.

"Do you not know that people are hungry, people are dying, wars are being started every other day, we are under occupation by a foreign invader?" we would be asked, time and again.

"Oh, yes," we'd say oh-so-very seriously, when the question had been answered, more than once in that particular conversation, but the answer had not been heard. "Perhaps we should just give up and die. Or how would you like us to put you out of your misery?"

Or sometimes we would really go to extremes—even for us. "You know, there's a planet on the other side of the Great Central Sun that would be just the place for you. Would you like us to send you there?"

"Do you think this is a joke?" sputtered the man we had just insulted.

"Yes, yes!" Yeshua exclaimed. "You got it! That's exactly what it is. A great, huge cosmic joke."

But before he lost his audience entirely, he put his hand on the man's shoulder and said, "My brother, I don't mean to minimize your pain, but cast your eyes upward. Don't keep them placed on the pain. Bring the Beloved who created all of Life into your daily life. Then all things will be made possible to you. We are all the liaison between Heaven and Earth. We are the very place where Earth meets Heaven, and we are to bring together both realms. That is our job. That is what we are here for."

☼

We were working with such simple people—people working the land with their hands, people casting their nets into the waters, people immersed in the physical and not giving much thought to the substance they could not touch. They were encased in fear and hardly thought much beyond the next five minutes, let alone to eternity. They were basically sleepwalking through life. But they had the innate wisdom of creation born in their bones and flowing through their veins. So they'd have those moments of awareness and understanding where they could see everything, know everything. And then it would close up again. It could be absolutely crazymaking for them, and I'm sure many preferred to just stay in the physical, even if it meant staying in the fear. It was easier and more familiar. But the intuition and deep perceptions would surface again, knocking on the door of their awareness.

Yeshua was here to help them open the door...to let them know that their keen insights, their flashes of tremendous wisdom were meant to be the norm, not the exception. He was here to wake them up from their fear-induced sleep.

And Yeshua himself came here to be the great example, not the great exception.

"What I can do, you can do, and greater things you will do, in the right time"—this is what he said. Take his words and climb upon them—this is what he wanted you to do. Live large, he emphasized again and again. People say they love this man who has become God to them...yet they insist on living their lives so much smaller than he wanted them to live, at just a tiny fraction of full capacity. What an insult both to him and to their supposed professed love for him!

Yeshua stood for love, peace, equality, dominion over the small self, and humility to the large Self. It is mind-boggling to consider the wars, fights, crusades, attempts to enslave or dominate...in his name. Have I told you I think this is beyond ridiculous? Yes, so I have. Forgive me for my repetition, but it bears repeating. Although you're not the one it bears repeating to. Could you please go tell the ones who need to hear?

Oh, of course, I know and I know you know, too: everything—everything!—serves a purpose...so there must have been a higher good for which the words had been so misconstrued. Sometimes we humans need a go-between to move from the first to the second step, if we've never climbed steps before. Sometimes we need to be saved—from ourselves, from the times we grew up in and became accustomed to, from the people who supposedly love us but are keeping us shrouded in fear, the same way they have been living their own lives.

Maybe we cannot go straight from lying in the street, reeling from unconsciousness, to knowing that we are the sons and daughters of Eternity. Fine, very well then. Sail on his wings as long as you need to. And then when the time is right, you'll find that his wings are your very own...and that his wings were never there to begin with, except in your mind.

For so many years, people needed that gentle, loving, guiding hand to hold on to. But there comes a time when you cross the street by yourself, after those years of holding tightly to your mother's hand. And there comes a time when you can transcend this world on your own. Now is the time.

*For God so loved the world, that he gave his only begotten Son....*

☼

Yes, God does so love the world. And She sent *all* of Her begotten children to save it.

☼

He taught well. He taught the great mysteries to vast crowds from vast walks of life. Perhaps some of it was casting pearls before swine (divine swine, to be sure), but the intent was to put it out there, and those who could take the information and use it, would; for those who could not yet use the information in their own lives, well, at least the seed was planted in their consciousness for it to bloom in the right time.

☼

Whoever thought that the right time would be two whole millennia later?

# CHAPTER 8

There was one particular way in which I was not particularly enlightened in that lifetime, and that was that I suffered from severe homesickness and missed the temple terribly on our trips. I was truly a very dedicated home and hearth person, and it was quite a stretch for me to be on the road for extended periods of time. But that is what Yeshua and I were called to do, and so we did it. When we do not do what we are clearly called to do, things can go dreadfully wrong!

Also, by now you know how the universe works and how sometimes our greatest fears can be our greatest teachings. And another way the universe works: if I didn't heal this particular trait of mine, I might find myself being on the road permanently. The universe so appreciates when we comprehend our lessons, and if we do not comprehend the lessons, the classwork becomes harder. So since I did not take to travel especially well and I knew how the universe works, it gave me the opportunity to concentrate on loving the road...or loving it as best I could, anyway. When the love was not flowing sufficiently from me, I would practice the art of growing—blooming, even—where planted...wherever I was, in that particular moment, it was my job to be there in that moment. That helped the love for the road flow a little better. But it was not always easy.

The journeys taught me that there is nowhere to go but here—right here, right now. There is nothing to have but what we have right now. There is nothing to do but be a better person than I was a moment ago. May this moment bring more patience, more love, more acceptance. May I be more of my true Self in this moment...and in this moment...and in this moment...and....

But I hated being dirty and far away from my wash basin and a neat pile of freshly laundered washing cloths. I loved the comfort of my own bed and the joy of waking up to only Yeshua—not of waking up to Yeshua along with a donkey trying to nuzzle my face and twenty-nine other people in extremely close proximity to us. I was grateful to know that my next meal was going to be delivered at a certain time as well as that I was near a well-scrubbed, sanitary place to eliminate that meal.

And I had to get over all that.

I had to keep my mind focused on the Mother Father God within more—not wash basins and beds—which strengthened my spiritual practice more. Every morning I would think of a new mantra for myself for the day and keep my mind focused on that one thing, whether it was the word "Beloved" or "Love" or "Peace" or phrases like "Love shines to me and from me" or "Peace fills my heart and radiates out to all I see." Sometimes I would sing my phrases as love songs to the Beloved—although not very loudly as my special gift to give in that life was definitely not my singing voice.

And sometimes nothing worked...I just wanted to go home.

I remember one day having a particularly hard time with the journey. No amount of trying to appreciate the thrill of the unknown or the adventure of the road could help assuage my longing for home. Usually when Mary, the Twelve, and I would assist with the numerous healings to be done, I could forget the heat and the dust and my thirst and my fatigue and my longing for home. But even seeing the hope on the faces of the people we were healing and teaching—which usually thrilled me—could not help me this particular time.

I never mentioned my homesickness but Yeshua sensed it. Often, no matter how full the day had been, he would make it a point to join me for evensong, just the two of us, away from the others. We would sit and meditate as the sun sank below the horizon, and then we would say our prayers together. Sometimes our prayers would go late into the night. Sometimes I'd fall asleep, and when I woke up in the early dawn, he would still be meditating. I have no idea how he did it. As I've told you, I needed my sleep and I needed food, especially on the road far from the familiar; he could go without either, any time, with nary a thought.

But that day, even despite our prayer and meditation time together, I was still utterly miserable. I was very seriously contemplating returning home, even if I had to walk the whole way by myself.

"What better way to teach people than to go to where they are?" Yeshua said to me, his eyes still shut in meditation, even though I had not breathed a word of my distress and possible pending decision. "See how they live and then reach them, right where they are? Even if it gets hard."

Sometimes I thought he should have been a mindreader in a traveling troubadour's show.

"Mary, just stay one more day, please?" He opened his eyes and flashed his dimples, which I did not think was playing fair.

Speaking of troubadours, we had plenty joining us on our journeys. Sometimes the musicians, poets, and storytellers would keep us up all night with their songs and tales. One highly accomplished musician could put Yeshua's teachings to song. He'd strum his lyre and proffer his deep, resonant voice to the night.

I pictured Yeshua's words traveling on the beautiful

melodies through the blackness, touching hearts and healing lives.

☼

The blue of the Great Sea met the blue of the sky; the white of the foam on the waters matched the clouds dotting the heavens. Somehow we found ourselves completely alone together, strolling along a stretch of beach. I looked behind us to see our footprints in the sand—two lines of prints, one large and one small, side by side. The sight made me smile.

Yeshua stopped abruptly, tore his clothes off, and dove into the azure waters. I dropped my robe but kept my under-robe on and paddled out to meet him. He could swim like a fish.

"Wouldn't you be much more comfortable without your robe on?" he laughed.

Even I would not undress anywhere outside my bedroom walls and present my body to the world. My hesitation and society's demand for my hesitation made no sense to me at all, because one of the most natural things in the world is the human body. But try telling the rest of society that, especially in those closed-minded days! The revolutionary ideas and practices on sexuality that I shared with many other people were protected by our bedroom doors and temple gates—I would never have divulged my thoughts and theories and activities to the public at large, at least not in that time. Your time is different. Many, many radical thoughts and theories have abounded over the ages; society can hear them now and even process them without subsequent crucifying, beheading, burning, or other means of silencing. Well, usually, at any rate.

I slipped my robe off over my head and Yeshua tossed it onto the beach, close to our other clothes. We floated together. The support of the cool water under my body contrasted with the heat of the sun warming my bare flesh thrilled me.

Even though there was still no one anywhere on the beach, I did not want to come out of the water until he retrieved my robe and threw it back to me. The hot afternoon sun and soft breeze dried our clothes as well as our bodies in mere moments. As my body adjusted to walking and not floating, however, my thoughts turned to home once again.

"Just stay one more day," he asked. And, once again, those dimples were just too irresistible. We took advantage of our alone time. And I stayed.

☼

That night we were lying in a field (perhaps if the accommodations had been more hospitable, I might have enjoyed the road more!), underneath a brilliant canopy of stars. The moon had not yet risen and the milky glow surrounding the stars radiated through the heavens. You know those moments: it was one of those nights and sights that absolutely fill your entire being with the wonder of Life.

I could hardly breathe—I was so enraptured with the grandeur of it. The area behind my ribs suddenly felt too small for the size my heart wanted to expand to. I forgot about my homesickness.

"I requested it, just for you," Yeshua whispered.

"I appreciate that," I smiled.

"Do you think it ever stops?" he asked me. "All that out there?"

"I don't think so," I answered. "After all, what would be on the other side of the edge? Something has to be there!"

Yeshua laughed. "I suppose you're right. Life is

eternal. The heavens must be eternal too."

A shooting star crossed the sky.

"What do you suppose that really is?" he asked.

"Mother Father God trying to help us remember?"

"Perhaps. And doing a great job." I could hear the smile in his voice. "I see colors, way out there."

I looked and the only color I could see, other than the usual yellow-gold sparkles across the pitch background, was a reddish star, low in the sky to the west.

"Well," I finally responded, "I cannot really see the colors but I can imagine them. In my mind I see colors spinning, making cocoons of light, birthing new stars."

"Do you suppose there are other places like ours, other worlds, where people like us live?"

"I would certainly guess that in an eternal universe such a thing would be possible."

"Do you suppose the people there understand it all a little better than the people here do?"

"I certainly hope so!" I laughed. "But that is what you are here for, to help the people in this place under-stand better."

"What a coincidence—that is what you are here for, too."

☼

And yet another coincidence—that is what you are here for, too.

☼

As radiant as the sun. As majestic as the Heavens. As awe-inspiring as the most delectable moment of your life. That's how Life beholds its most magnificent masterpiece:

You.

☼

Nowadays you would refer to what he was doing as giving me a pep talk. The next day we started in the direction of the city and the time that became famous for what you know as the Sermon on the Mount. I was so happy that I had not gone home.

☼

We found ourselves day after day after day in the hot sunshine. In addition to my difficulties with travel, I also detested intense heat, which was certainly a serious problem for someone who lived in a part of Earth that could be intensely hot.

During the day his mother and I were mostly on the side, quiet; we would seek out the shade, if there was any, and pray and meditate for hours while Yeshua taught and preached to the crowds that gathered around him. Sometimes I would ask her a question that would require a long answer, just to hear her beautiful voice, which was soothing and cool, like a gentle stream rambling over rocks. Sometimes we would fall silent, and I would return to my word or mantra practice to keep my mind focused on the love instead of the weather and abhorrent conditions...well, they were abhorrent to me. I'm sure the scorpions liked the heat and dryness.

Yeshua was clearly at one with his inner scorpion because these conditions did not bother him in the slightest. I suppose I could have tried to access my inner scorpion as well...but I actually think I did fairly well overall, considering.

On that one particular day we were gathered on a

hillside. The sun was high in the sky already, blazing down on us. There was no shade to be seen anywhere. I wondered if I could slip away easily and unobtrusively but instead somehow, miraculously, slipped into prayer and meditation. The crowd was becoming larger—it looked to be about five thousand, perhaps more, and it was growing by the moment.

Yeshua started to speak. "Blessed are those who give their hearts to the Mother Father God that created us all, for they truly live in Heaven on Earth." Unfortunately, I believe you have heard this as *"Blessed are the poor in spirit; for theirs is the kingdom of heaven."*

I floated off on wings of love, carried on the warm air currents, which were created by his words. My body unwound as I laid back, resting on the Earth and letting her wrap her loving arms around me. I shut my eyes and could feel the energy of the crowd. I felt an opening in the hearts, minds, and souls of so many of the people there. They were starving for the words he was feeding them.

*"Blessed are the peacemakers: for they shall be called the children of God."*

Yes, that was the same then as you hear it now.

Oh, my beloved (yes, you), no one had talked like that before this day. For this one afternoon the fear, the anger, the scarcity consciousness, the hatred of the oppressors, the limited belief system left the people of that crowd, and they basked in the light of his words.

*"The light of the body is the eye: if therefore thine eye be single, thy whole body shall be full of light."*

You've been hearing these words for two thousand years. Just imagine what it was like to hear them for the very first time! My heart was overflowing with gratitude. Pressed down, running over. The scorching sunshine and the heat no longer bothered me. I could feel the ripples through the crowd as his words were heard, and then another ripple as his words were understood, and then yet one more ripple as his words were appreciated.

"*Ye are the light of the world. A city that is set on a hill cannot be hid. Neither do men light a candle, and put it under a bushel, but on a candlestick; and it giveth light unto all that are in the house. Let your light so shine before* all people, *that they may see your good works, and glorify* Mother Father *God* that is everywhere present."

☼

I remembered addressing a student's anxiety in this regard. Actually, I had this conversation at least once a year, with each new crop of pupils.

"Sometimes I'm afraid if I shine my light fully, I'll be swallowed whole by the thirst and hungers of others who are starving for this light. Like parasites!"

"Well, the first thing to do," I told her, "is not to refer to them as parasites, but as people who haven't found their own light yet and are attracted to yours."

"They're light-suckers," she said. "Like bloodsuckers."

"How about light-seekers?" I suggested. "That's a much higher term. And then you're lifted up to that higher level, and they'll catch the rising air current."

"But they try to suck me dry when I let my light so shine before them! And then where would I be? I might as well hide it."

"I had a similar fear when I first started learning how powerful I am," I told her. "And I was instructed then and now I'll instruct you to put on an armor of light, every day, before going out into the world. You can draw this armor of light around you, like a garment, and instruct it to allow only good to permeate its shell and come to you, and to keep out everything less than good."

She nodded.

"You cannot keep yourself to yourself." I laughed at the confused look on her face. Gradually she understood my words. "You cannot keep your light and power and love and joy to yourself. You must be generous with it. That is why you develop it so carefully. That is why we teach these things to you—so you can go forth and spread them. And not for your benefit, but for the benefit of all, including the one who brought you here. That's one of the secrets of life."

☼

Actually, there are a great many secrets of life. Want to know what they are? Here:

We all have moments of peak awareness—when we truly understand the great mystery. Cultivate those moments.

Die daily to your old way of thinking, to the you that was yesterday.

Pray without ceasing.

Know that thoughts are things. Know that the thoughts you are thinking right now—RIGHT NOW—are your prayers that are creating your tomorrow, and the day after, and the day after that. How do you want your tomorrow to be? Think—pray—on those things.

Every thought—well, at least the second, third, fourth, fifth thought—is a choice. (The first thought might slip in from time to time, straight out of the quagmire that can be our race consciousness, and we wonder, "Where in the world did this judgment/slur/complaint/reaction/griping come from?" We might not be one-hundred percent responsible for the first thought that arises, but all the ones that come after it are our full responsibility.)

Think of a person who is completely filled with the Holy Spirit, the Buddha, the Christ—whatever you want to call the Presence of God—and emulate him or her. Let yourself be filled with the Presence of God...and know that this is you, making yourself known to yourself.

Forgive others as quickly as you can...not for their sake but for yours.

If you don't love what you do, do yourself—and the world—a favor and find what you love and do it. The world does not need more people slaving just to make a living. The world needs more people *living*...living their love, their joy, their peace, their beauty.

If you cannot do what you love, for now, at least infuse what you do with love. Sell that trinket, move that piece of paper, lift that load with love. The love will spread and call more of itself into your life. And do what you absolutely love, at least for a few moments a day. Your life and even the whole world will be lifted by your higher vibration. And then you will find yourself doing what you love.

Honor thy mother and father. Do what would make them proud. Fulfill their promise without denying your own call. Actually it would be impossible to do one without the other, because the fulfilling of the agreement you made when you incarnated will both answer your call and fulfill their promise for you.

Know that Heaven is at hand: Heaven is within. You have the ability to access Heaven in any moment. Access this inner presence now and gain access to whatever you want: abundance, joy, everything divine. It is always there. The difference in whether you experience it or not is......choice.

Know that Life can be as beautiful and glorious as

you want. Your mission—and, yes, part of you has already chosen to accept it—is to let Life be Life...and then just sit back and marvel.

☼

"Teacher," someone called out from the midst of the large gathering, "show us how to pray."

Yeshua took a moment to center himself on the Earth while lifting his hands to the skies. "Beloved Mother Father God, Creator of all things, how holy are your names. We lift this time up, as a holy and sacred moment...as holy and sacred as any that have gone before, and as are any yet to come. Thank you for this day, our *daily bread*. Thank you for the gifts of your bounty. For thou art within me, around me, everywhere present, now and always. And so it is."

Yes, I understand you might have heard that a little differently, too. In Aramaic, *Abba* can be literally translated as Father, but at the time it also meant Beloved, can refer to any very close relationship, and does not necessarily apply to one gender or the other. *Abba* could mean any beloved, whether a parent, child, sibling, lover, or friend relationship—in addition to God/ Goddess/All That Is. The relationship between a Father and Son was highly revered at the time, but this usage was not necessarily meaning just a Father and Son—it could have meant the Beloved and any of Its children.

☼

Do you want to know how to pray? Stop asking for things and seek just to show up as love. And then, of course, by then you do not need or care if you have things, which then allows them to be "added to you" by Grace. Have you ever noticed that once you did not need to have the object of your desire, it then came, with no effort? So we can move beyond praying for the objects of our desires. And then anything we desire shows up, of its own accord.

"Lord, make me an instrument," Francis of Assisi prayed. So many have prayed these words, too. How many have really meant them? How about this:

Oh, beloved Mother Father God, use me, mold me, let me be your instrument. Beloved Mother Father God, Creator of all that is, take my hand and guide it to where it performs its highest good. Through my mouth speak words of truth. Through my hands allow me to touch, heal, transform others. Through my eyes shine rays of love. Through my heart guide me to give your greatest service. Through my being allow me to live your highest purpose. Guide me to my right place today, with the right words, the right actions. Guide me to where I can be your smile to ease someone's heartache, your healing power to ease someone's pain. What words of your wisdom would you have me say? What is it you would have me do this moment, this day, this lifetime? Beloved Mother Father God, creator of all that is...this is the day that you have made. Let me celebrate it. Let me be your emissary. Let me exalt in your love. Let me be a living, breathing, walking representation of your love. Let me share this with every being I see today—uplifting and inspiring them to do the same.

There. How's that? A little different from the age-old beseeching method, is it not?

☼

Who, exactly, is this divine entity we are praying to? Who is this Mother Father God, Beloved, Creator? It is the All that is everywhere and lives within each of us.

We may not be all of the All, but all we are comprised of is the All. There is nothing about us that is not a piece of the All in form.

When we pray, we are not wooing a reluctant, petulant, noncompliant God for good things to come to us. We are becoming clear in ourselves about the Good we may do and partake in. Prayer does not convince God of anything; prayer illuminates for us where we are now and where we want to be. Prayer provides clarity. Prayer takes us from our small personality to our place in the whole.

I, as Mary, have nothing to say. I, as the piece of the Divine that I am, have everything to say. I, as the fearful, limited human, have nothing to say. I, as a drop of the Beloved in the divine ocean, have everything to say. I, as the frail human with the bloated pride to mask my frailty, have nothing to say. I, as the emissary of the Cosmos, have everything to say.

Prayer, done aright, throws opens the doorway from our inner divine to the outer.

So, who is talking? And who is listening? Determine that....And then when the answer to both is I AM, prepare the message.

I am a divine conduit, as is any teacher, artist, or great master, being guided from beyond my own small self. I of myself can do nothing. I am assisted by the sublime divinity that exists everywhere, steered by Love to create masterpieces, teach, share, and heal.

The only way to pray for something specific is to give thanks and bless what you already have, as Yeshua did with the loaves and fishes. Next give thanks for the situation or increase as though you already have it. And then bestow love, love, and more love upon your life and the things you desire.

Have you ever seen an extraordinarily beautiful garden? Or an extraordinarily rich man of business? Or a family with extraordinarily well-behaved and joy-filled children? Or an extraordinarily sublime piece of art? They are all a product of love. Flowers flourish under the hand of love, as do children, as does money, as does a piece of artwork. These laws do not work for some and then not for others. Anyone who bestows love on his or her creation will see it flourish. What we focus on expands.

But it is even more than that. We are not living in a mental universe; we are living in a spiritual universe, where God is all-encompassing. A true understanding and embodiment of these words will bring all the added things. So live in the enormity of it all, and bless and love it all. The level of peace, joy, abundance that comes into your life is equal to your level of spiritual awareness.

And you cannot always just bless, give thanks, and love things and then expect a wealthy merchant to show up with baskets of bread and fish. Although that can certainly happen at times. And did.

☼

My beloved, something very important to know, as well, is that it is not so much the prayer itself as it is the time between the prayers. It is every thought and action between those prayers—*every* thought, *every* action... *every*thing is a prayer. It is all a prayer. Let the business you are building, the meal you are making, the field you are tilling be your prayer. Let the bedtime routine with your child, the morning ablutions, the mid-day break be your prayer. Let your midnight lovemaking and afternoon chats be your prayer. Let it all be a remembrance of the Divine, let it all be the lovesong of your heart, let it all be your praise of Life.

And even if you are sitting by yourself at some point

during the day, feeling somewhat melancholy or regretful of something or another, focus on the love. And the entire universe will be affected. By you.

As you sit by the hearth, focus on your heart. Let your love infuse the food you are preparing for your family's evening meal. This love will pass through the food and into your family members. The love will fill up your family, radiate from them, and illumine the world.

And if you find yourself alone at the end of the day—if you are an old woman whose family has moved on to distant places, if you are a young man who has just left home to start your own journey, whoever you are—infuse your own evening meal with love. And the whole world will be transformed.

☼

Ultimately we all move toward the highest, simplest prayer of all: Thank You. And then even beyond that, we move to living in the serene silence where we spread our arms in the allness of God, where all has been given and our gratitude is felt, even to the very farthest star.

# CHAPTER 9

That unpleasant trait of mine—the one that did not allow me to enjoy the road nearly as much as I could have—made all of our homecomings incredibly, inordinately joyous. Some of the most exquisite moments of those days were the returns from our journeys to the smells of the herbs, oils, incense, ointments, and perfumes that filled our quarters. The garden right outside our door, while small in size, was large in beauty and pungent smells, as well. Olive and fig trees covered the palace grounds, giving us much needed shade as well as the offerings of their branches. The air was thick with the scent of new possibilities, the scent that announced, "Something very, very special happens here." The aroma greeted us and welcomed us home.

I would fall into our bed, arms outstretched, just inhaling the powerful scents and exalting in the feeling of my scrumptious bed underneath me. And I would stay that way for hours.

We still lived at the temple palace, which was unusual. Not many couples stayed at the temple once they were married, but we were very comfortable there. I still had so much I wanted to do for the many young students, and it was the perfect place for me while Yeshua traveled solo, so we stayed.

It is so interesting that my name means "a bitter mix of herbs." It is also so interesting that so many of us back then were named Mary. It was more of a designation than a name, in many situations. *Mary......* announced that a healer was at work in this place.

Have you ever wondered why healers act so crazy at

times? Living in the higher planes and then having to walk on a dense planet can be extremely difficult. It can be crazymaking. I know I've mentioned this in regards to the high place that Yeshua and I lived compared to the society we lived in. Sometimes the crashing from one world to another would practically make me a mad-woman.

When I was a young healer I would sometimes find myself stuck for hours as I was moving from one world to another, nearly crazed and probably a menace to be near. Age, wisdom, and years of practice eased this dilemma, but sometimes even as I grew older I would still let myself be thrown off center. For instance, I would find myself caught in the throngs of people in the marketplace, wondering about the crazy rush around me. Where was everyone going? And why were they in such a hurry? It was the days when I did *not* notice that really told me where I was...because it was when I did not notice the hustle and bustle that I had become part of it myself.

It is such a delicate balance to walk. There is such a fine line between our worlds. Sometimes it is enough to make anyone mad. Those who walk among us, babbling to themselves or to some unseen (to the rest of us, anyway) beings, are the ones with the most difficult time. Back then people like that were referred to as having devils that needed casting out. As we have already discussed, Yeshua was certainly noted for numerous castings out of devils, but, as you know now, what he did was bring those people more fully into this dimension. Actually, he offered them the permission, opportunity, and opening to finally arrive into this dimension with all their faculties. There are no devils in anyone, anywhere, anyway. Satan is a myth created by people who did not understand and who had to have the duality of good versus evil in order to create a more satisfactory understanding of the mystery for themselves.

☼

As you probably know, there was an account that Peter chastised Yeshua for my using expensive, new herbs and ointments on his feet and head. This event actually happened long before our last night together— it was not for Yeshua's burial, as was told.

"That money could have gone to the poor!" Peter chided him. "They are more important than your feet and head!"

And, woe the day. No, as I already told you, my beloved never, ever said that there will be poor always. Is that not a rather strange thing for him to have said, given everything else you have heard about him? No, there will not be poor always. That is part of our job, to ensure the continuing evolution of the planet, and that means higher standards of health, wealth, living, being. That does not mean we give away all of our money, although giving what we can helps at times. It means we live our lives as best we can, being an example, teaching the allness of Life and Love to those who would hear. A mighty tree does not grow quickly, and neither would perfection on Earth, but it is the mighty tree's job to grow, and it is our job—and our honor—to do our part in bringing about perfection. It does not mean to be hypervigilant. It can be fun, joyous, easy, graceful, delightful. It does not mean to go with less so that others can have more; there is enough for us all... within reason, of course, and as long as our actions are for the good of all and the harm of none.

So the money that went to the ointments and herbs went to the people who prepared and grew them as well as to their families. The money that goes to opulent, lavish living goes on to many sources—feeding children and keeping home and hearth together for the growers, makers, producers, creators of beautiful things. I do not mean we should squander money on wasteful nonsense, but sharing money on the things we love feeds the soul as well as literally feeds many, many others.

On a higher level we are all given everything. The mystics taught this then and still teach it now. Yeshua certainly taught it over and over, as did I, and we are still teaching—to you, now. Some understood it back then, but even today many refuse to believe that the domain of Heaven is within. Within! All of us! There is no one exempt from this. There is not one place where God does not reside in divine splendor, and that means that God resides in divine splendor in each one of us.

We do not pray for things. Well, naturally we do, but we ought not to. As I mentioned a little earlier, to pray aright, we bless and love what we have, but we also pray to know the allness of God, and then all things are added unto us. But if one is hungry, that does not exactly work. Basic things must be taken care of first. If we have starving people, we have people who will fight to the death for any scrap, of anything. And there is starving for not only food, but also for love, power, justice, tolerance—but let's start with food. There is no reason that anyone should be hungry on a planet that has plenty. There is no reason for poverty; there is no reason that there would be poor always.

☼

*Christ* means "the anointed one." Those herbs, ointments, and oils were what I used to anoint him. I washed his feet and anointed his crown. The money spent fed many people.

Tell me the money could have been used better elsewhere.

☼

Holy Mother Father God, in this sacred moment, in this sacred place, I put my hand over the third eye of this most holy and sacred person—the person reading these words, right here and right now.

I open my jar of ointment, mixed with oils and a bitter, spicy, sweet aroma fills the room. I touch your forehead. You have a flash of recognition, of remembering.

You are now anointed...although you were already anointed and have been since the beginning of time. You have been a Christ since the beginning of time... and now you are awake to it.

☼

Do you understand, my beautiful beloved? If so, do you live as an anointed one, a Christed one? If not yet, when would you like to? When would you like to be in charge of your entire experience, devote your life to love, and dance through your days in ecstasy?

☼

Yeshua sat in the main garden of the palace, his back against a rock, deep in contemplation. I sat down beside him. He did not open his eyes but he smiled at me. We sat in meditation, separate but together, joined at every level of our beings.

I heard the music again, not from any one instrument, and not from any one person playing, at least not in this world. I looked at him, and by the smile on his face I knew he heard it, too. The spheres were singing to both of us. He opened his eyes for a moment to look at me in concurrence. We meditated for a while longer and then both started to stand at the same time.

"You are the only one who understands what I say," he said. "And I do not even have to say anything."

I smiled and took his hand as we walked back to our quarters, our own small palace, our own Heaven on Earth.

☼

In every lifetime there is a moment where we understand...where we understand that all the trials and tribulations brought us to this very place and time. It is a moment where our hearts crack open and we are able to love more than before, love the Beloved and both ourselves and our beloveds, along with anyone else around us...even strangers on the other side of creation. It is a moment of realization that life was created through, as, and by Love. Love is in complete control of the moment, and it can carry us on gossamer wings to new heights and awaken us to new depths within our beings. We understand...all of it. It does not matter what the future may require of us; things can come as they may, because we will always carry this moment within us. This is *the* moment of *this* particular life.

Yeshua and I stood, facing each other. I placed my hand on his heart. He put his hand over mine and then placed his other hand on my heart, where I put my other hand over his. We gazed into each other's eyes. The entire world disappeared except for the radiant pools of love and light that were his eyes. I knew he saw the same radiant pools in mine.

Yeshua put his hand on my face, and I felt the thrill of his touch in every cell and fiber of my entire being. His mouth touched mine, and I heard the hum again as the world completely faded away and dissolved to just the sense of our lips pressed together and our tongues touching. But after a moment he ran his hands over my body, awakening my world to places beyond my mouth.

He slipped my robes off and I lay down on the bed. The room was flooded with sunshine, which seemed more brilliant than usual. The gentle wind brought the garden up to us—the scent of the flowers filled the room. He slipped his own robe off and stood over me, gazing at me for a long moment, smiling, and then slowly joined me on the bed. I rolled on top of him. Our bodies pressed together, connected in that so very primal yet so very sublime way, and we moved in unison, creating waves that cascaded over us, lifting us higher and higher until they crashed in a shuddering crescendo for both of us at the very same moment. We lay together, completely exhilarated. Every sense was wide awake, on high alert, as the vibrant throbs pulsating through my entire body slowly subsided, replaced with a luscious calm and tranquility, even greater than usual, which radiated throughout all levels of my being.

We listened to the birds as they sang sweetly from their perches high in the trees outside the front door. I found myself hoping that no one had been right outside our window. Ah, well, if there had been anyone, he or she would have heard the sounds of love being shared and probably would have been inspired to go share the same kinds of sounds with his or her beloved one.

The blazing afternoon sun started to become very hot on us, and Yeshua pulled the curtain closed. The sunshine pierced a few of the tiny holes in the fabric design of the curtains, casting unusual patterns as the light played on the wall across the room.

I was so in love—wrapped up in it, encompassing it, playing with it, being enveloped by it, reveling in it, laughing with it. And its name was Yeshua. And its name was Mary. And its name was anyone, anything, anywhere, at any time because at that moment there was absolutely nothing outside of this love.

One thing about love: its major joy is to create more of itself.

☼

My mother told me time and again that she knew the instant a new life had started within her, my entrance into this world. "It was as if my whole body started to rejoice that you were coming, to welcome you here," she said. It was the most loving, high-level thing she shared with me.

I looked down at my own body that had just started to rejoice in a new life coming. There was a fluttering deep inside me—I was not sure if it was physical or ethereal. Probably both. My breasts felt fuller, riper and my nipples were tender to the touch. I welcomed this new being with all my being.

Yeshua had gone to the hills to meditate for a few days while I was overseeing several major events at the temple. When he returned he stood in the doorway for a while, looking at me. He was puzzled at first as he looked at my face, gazed at the field around my body, and then looked at my breasts and stomach. He smiled.

He walked over to me and gently put his hand on my belly as he kissed the top of my head.

"She will look just like you," he said.

"How do you know it is a she?"

"I know."

So did I. Tears filled my eyes. "My king," I

whispered.

His tears matched mine. "My queen."

☼

Every day, for the rest of my life—especially when I gazed upon the beautiful being that came into being that beautiful day—I remembered how sweetly the birds were singing...how the sun was shining in the room that afternoon...how the unusual patterns of light danced on the walls...how the hot breeze brought the perfume of the garden up to us...and how much love was expressed, shared, and celebrated in the creation of her.

# CHAPTER 10

The dream clutched my throat, holding back my screams. I slowly realized I was awake but the dream still held me captive.

"Mary, darling, what is it?"

His arms enveloped me, helping the dream to dissipate like morning mist. But I could not tell him.

In my dreams I often traveled the world (I enjoyed traveling in this fashion much more than in the body!) and talked to people of the planet: children in the sizzling hot, barren lands on an island continent. Villagers in the lush, green lands to the south. Men in the icy lands to the north. Women on islands dotting a great ocean. They are all so beautiful. I see the disparity of the sexes and the subjugation of women and pray with them for the time when they will be on equal status. In some places I see the subjugation of the men, as well, and I pray with them for their time of equality, too. I see people enslaved and pray with them for the time when all can finally recognize their own divinity enough to see it in everyone around them and can no longer engage in slavery, war, corruption. I see the joy and freedom of the children, almost everywhere, before they let fear grab hold of their hearts. We share our knowledge—I tell them all the things that I know; they tell me the things that they know.

But this dream showed years, decades, centuries of unrest, turmoil—much of it in my beloved Yeshua's name. Women burned alive. Groups of people poisoned by noxious fumes. An enormous cloud obliterating life for many hundreds of miles. An increase of male domination. It was all done in his name but not for anything he stood for. His words were twisted for the profit of a few instead of the good of the many. His life became a manipulation of the populace, through fear. His beautiful teachings fell by the wayside while very strange abominations were done in his name: killings, suppressings, a smothering of the breath of life, an extinguishing of our inner light.

And I could not tell him what I saw, what I felt, what I was pondering in my heart. I knew he had to continue on his mission of teaching, and I could not tell him anything that would slow him down.

The previous night our ceremonial oil lamp broke mysteriously, just as we were about to fall asleep. Yeshua was baffled about why I was so inordinately upset. And I did not want to talk with him about what I knew it portended.

But he knew. Of course he did. And he did the best thing he could have done—held me while I cried and cried and cried. And cried. And cried.

☼

There is a legend from the lands far, far to the east, even farther than Yeshua traveled on his journey those earlier years. An empress—you know who she is, Kwan Yin—was going to enter Heaven but she heard the plaintive cries of humanity and decided to stay on Earth until everyone could enter Heaven.

We are all going there. But some of us have to be the emissaries, the teachers.

And some of us have to die.

☼

Yes, some of us have to die...to get the teaching across. For the good of the whole. For the much bigger picture. Life is temporary anyway. Dying is just one part of the game. Some of us have to die. Some of us have to die.

I was starting to be able to say that to myself. I found it hard to imagine that the world would truly be better off if he were silenced. But I also knew that perhaps one who has been silenced can convey a louder message that way.

And what better way to show the truth of eternal life than...to die?

☼

But he never said—never meant to imply, never even hinted—that through his life and his death was he the only way to God. Through his life and his death what he wanted to say was, "Wake up!"

☼

Religions were formed as an explanation for the many things that mystified people, yes, and every religion is based on a divine spark of truth and love. Every religion is a path to God. But no one idea is right for everyone. Everyone has a personal path to follow.

So all religions take people closer to the God of their understanding, and for that I am grateful. The world is a far better place for people's closer walk with God. (Oh, shudder to think what it would be like without this closer walk!) We can take anything based in love from any of the world's great religious traditions, philosophies, works of art, feats of science—anything, really. However...I do not mean to disparage anyone's beliefs, but if someone's beliefs involve the redemption of a few and the suffering of the many, it is time for those beliefs to stop. If someone's beliefs involve righteous indignation, hatred, and intolerance, it is time for those beliefs to stop. It is high time for people to stop dying in the name of fairy tales, myths, exclusivity, holier-than-thou attitudes, beliefs in a chosen people—whether Christian, Jewish, Muslim, or any other religion or sect. We are all chosen. We are here, we are God in form, and we are *all* chosen—*every one of us.*

Mankind (and please notice I said mankind, not humanity) has been searching for excuses to perpetuate war on each other since the beginning. I do not like to presuppose the divine plan, but perhaps that was a "bug," as you would say nowadays, in the early proto-cols of the human species. I am jesting, of course; there are no accidents. Wars are part of the learning process, unfortunately.

But Yeshua was so adamantly opposed to war. And to think of all the wars that have taken place in his name over the last two thousand years—self-righteous, arrogant, ignorant men with bibles under one arm and swords, daggers, shields, bayonets, muskets, AK 47's, ballistic missiles under the other arm. Does anyone else see anything strange about that image? Yes, of course I realize the missiles cannot be tucked under one arm...but many who press the button to fire them have a bible nearby, at least in mind if not in the physical. Does anyone else see anything strange about that image, too? Well, perhaps after my railing about the bible, the image may not seem to be all that strange any more.

In my day we had come a long way from the many gods of our ancestors, but we were still in the throes of a society that insisted on a judgmental, capricious, patriarchal, war-mongering God. Even two thousand years have done little to obliterate the belief of this kind of God for many people.

We shared esoteric teachings of the esoteric laws of living. I taught them within the temple walls and Yeshua taught them to crowds on the hillsides and in the city streets. The esoteric teachings of the esoteric laws of living give the power to everyone. This is nothing to be fearful of...unless you happen to want to be in control. And then you fear losing control. And one way to keep control is to keep people in fear—especially of each other.

"But I say unto you," he truly did say, "Love your enemies, bless them that curse you, do good to them that hate you, and pray for them which despitefully use you, and persecute you."

☼

So in the meantime, while we are waiting for everyone to wake up to the fact that there is only one of us here, what conscious people can do is pray for both those who feel separate from God and those who feel they have the exclusive route to God. My words may seem exclusive to those who have beliefs different from mine and Yeshua's. But our teachings are based on love—the eternal truth of love. We do not put down, revile, judge anyone; nor do we put ourselves higher than anyone. We know that all people are on a personal path of personal evolution. In the whole great, divine scheme of things, everyone is right where he or she is meant to be.

And we will all get to where we are going.

☼

In this most holy and sacred moment, on this most holy and sacred spot, with this most holy and sacred person (that would be you), I turn my attention to the

Mother Father God that dwells within me, that dwells within each person, each thing, in all of creation. And it is simply in this remembering that I am made whole. It is in this remembering that I am complete. There is no peace out there that I must add to myself to experience peacefulness...I am peace already. There is no love out there that I must add to my life to experience love...I am love already. There is no joy out there that I must entice into my life in moments here and there...I am joy already. There is no abundance out there that I must add to my day to experience wealth...I am abundance already. I am peace, love, joy, and abundance. This is who and what I am. This is who and what we all are... and our only path to this experience is in the remembering.

There is no God out there, no distant deity that I must beseech, beg, petition, bargain with...I am God in form. I am not all of God but all that I am is God. And it is not I who does the work but the Mother Father God that dwells within me, that is me at my highest level, that does the work. I give thanks that I know this, and I give thanks that my brothers and sisters are coming to know this, as well. I give thanks for the highest good for all unfolding. I give thanks for the awakening in the hearts of everyone, everywhere, right now. So be it.

☼

It is happening. So be it.

☼

One of the strangest things to me is one particular line attributed to him: *"Except a man be born again, he cannot see the kingdom of God."* First of all, he never would have said just "man"; he would have been more inclusive than that. Second, as I've told you, he never would have said a gender-biased word like kingdom—he always referred to that region, realm, place, whatever of Heaven as the domain of Heaven. Third, he only referred to the domain of Heaven as within AND without, never just without, and certainly not far and away from each of us. And fourth, he never meant that line to be used for separatism, elitism, sectarianism, exclusivity, holier-than-thou-ness, the A-list of God's children, the chosen few. Being born again simply means to be renewed, regenerated. We can do that every moment of our lives.

His entire message was one of inclusiveness—that we are *all* so very loved, we are *all* so very special, we are *all* chosen. I am completely flummoxed by the people following what they think are his words and not being in inclusiveness. Is it just me or….Anyway, Yeshua said time and again that we are all children of God, we are all extraordinary.

I would suppose that, way back when, certain groups survived better than they might otherwise have survived because the knowledge (albeit false) that they were the chosen ones lifted them higher and farther. But what about the ones who still think that today? There is no special group more privileged, more entitled, more anything. No one group is more "in" with God. No one is more likely to enter Heaven than another. Heaven is at hand…literally.

I know there is a very famous picture in a very famous place depicting my beloved as casting sinners into hell. Yeshua would never, EVER cast anyone into eternal damnation. Eternal damnation is a figment of someone's imagination anyway; it does not exist. But if it did, Yeshua would certainly be trying to rescue the souls sent there, not sending more to its fiery pits.

Exclusivity is harmful to many. Unfortunately, the

ones who practice exclusivity the most are the ones least likely to read or hear my words.

But as a whole group we are moving beyond that now, evolving to a higher place, even though it may not appear that way. We are not done here until we are all fully here. All of us. No one gets left behind.

☼

Speaking of evolution...both sides of the argument on evolution are correct. Life evolves. And God/Goddess guides the evolution of all of Its creations.

Now let us move on from that, shall we?

☼

And speaking of putting ourselves higher (or not, as the case may be), sometimes when we have been gifted with great talents, treasures, gifts, and knowledge—and have enormous crowds of people hanging on our every word, as Yeshua found himself—it can be challenging to not have a holier-than-thou attitude creep up from time to time. But the Universe has a way of balancing the scales when that attitude comes up. It knows how to bring us back to Earth and to get us humble again. So we might as well stay humble in the first place. There is no one on Earth better than us, and there is no one on Earth less than us. No one!

We might encounter people in our travels with great disadvantages, either conditions they have come in with or conditions they have brought on themselves. How can we honor their decision to be like that? Well, we do not know what they have chosen to learn...or teach. Perhaps they have chosen that almighty lesson of loving themselves no matter what they present to the outside world and how the outside world responds to them. Or maybe they have chosen to teach those around them patience. Benevolence. Love. Humility.

One of the primary things that Yeshua and I taught to our respective students was that each person has a divine purpose, a reason for being......that if you were not here, the secret in your heart that you came in with would not be revealed for the betterment of us all. So no one *could* be more special than another. We all have that secret to be revealed, somehow, in the right time, in the right place.

Yeshua's whole life was about taking our teachings out to touch the whole world. The teachings he presented were based on love—pure, simple, unadulterated, unconditional love. They were so absolutely amazing, so utterly exquisite, so powerful. How could they get so confused? How could they get so turned around to be used in such destructive ways? Imagine killing in the name of someone who stood for love. Imagine judging in the name of someone who stood for forgiveness, compassion, and acceptance.

Now, about the fishes and the loaves...obviously we could not feed five thousand people with just a few fishes and a little bit of bread. Joseph, the wealthy merchant I referred to earlier, had arranged for baskets of food to be brought from the newly arriving ships to the multitudes just at the time that Yeshua was blessing what we had. Joseph supported many of our journeys, as did other men and women of means, as did the temple. When I mention Joseph, I am referring to Joseph of Arimathea. Yeshua's father, Joseph, while a wonderful man, had little to do with Yeshua's life during my years with him.

The story grew that a miracle had happened, and perhaps it had, if you call right timing a miracle, which of course it is.

☼

We fed five thousand, with the miracle of right timing. And we had no wires or signals that crisscross the Earth, connecting all of humanity at the speed of light. Oh, imagine what you can do now.

☼

And then do it. Please. After all, it is what you agreed to do when you agreed to come here.

☼

It is wonderful to live in the extraordinary places that we create for ourselves, but that is not necessarily where our true growth happens. The silence is where we go to fill up, but it is the loudness of everyday living that strengthens us, too. It is not meditating alone, it is not sitting alone in caves or on the desert, although those times serve us, often very deeply—it is when we meet life on Earth face to face, sometimes in very strange places...and accept it...and do everything we can to make it better.

It is easy to love those who love you, and it is so much harder to pray for those who despitefully use you, to quote my beloved somewhat. And sometimes it is easier to take the lower road. Some people get away with lying, stealing, manipulating—for years! But for those of us who know, a slight transgression can have immediate, thorough repercussions. Spirituality can wreak havoc on the lower level desires and those who pursue them.

And speaking of being in strange places...well, we just never know. We might be in a strange place, crazy even, far beyond anything we ever would have thought up of our own accord, but we might be the only words of the Divine that someone gets to hear. We might set them on a much straighter path to God. We have been used for a greater purpose—which is an answer to both our prayers and theirs.

Sometimes it is hard to believe that the planet gets along as well as it does, given some of the most intelligent and powerful people in the world are cut-throat, egotistical, voraciously greedy, even corrupt.

I was talking about Jerusalem at the dawn of the first millennium—what were you thinking of? Oh, yes, right, it has not changed as much as it could have.

So how can we see and maintain the higher picture while living in a world of petty squabbles, shameless gluttony, and rampant destruction? Our job is to see the Divine in everyone...and then meet them where they are.

You need not worry about how the others will get it. Just rise and they will rise with you. And if there is something in your life that no longer serves you, just rise and it will fall away, because it cannot rise that high. Your main mission: to rise. Be higher than the person you were last year, yesterday, ten seconds ago. And don't worry about having to preach on a mountainside, the way Yeshua did, or in a classroom, the way I did. Just shine your highest self; that will be preaching enough.

Of course you already know all this. I am not telling you anything you have not heard. It is just good to be reminded, is it not? It can be so hard to hold the higher levels on and on without the reminders, especially in a world that experiences things very differently. Yes, it is good to be reminded—again and again and again. And again. And then even after that.

And so we cultivate our peak times. We all have peak moments where we know...we feel the connection, we see the whole of creation in the palm of a hand, in one tiny flower, in the motion of a bird in flight...we sense the movement of life through us and thrill to it, ride the wave of ecstasy. Those are the moments we are truly alive. It is so hard to sustain that. Then we come crashing back to the denseness of the planet. Yeshua and our friends and I were very advanced compared to the people around us. Now you have many pockets of awake and aware people, all over the planet, and more awakening every day. And still it is hard.

We *all* came to have life and have it more abundantly. We are *all* daughters and sons of the Most High. We came here to be, do, have, delight in everything, even soar through the galaxies. We do not have to be so expanded out into the cosmos, however, that we are not of any good down here on Earth. The idea is to be expanded where we are sitting, right here, right now, with our partners, with our families, with our tribes, with our villages, with our nations, with our world. We are to live in all our dimensions—body, mind, spirit, the temple of the soul, the temple of the home, the Earth so cleverly devised for our evolution—and all the dimensions of our outer world, as well, from near to far. Mastery of this dimension is as important as mastery of the other dimensions.

Our bodies are amazingly incredible, spectacular vehicles designed to take us wherever we want to go. Our minds are part of the Divine Intelligence. We can do anything, go anywhere...let's just make sure it is somewhere wonderful, for all of us. It will happen. It is happening. It is unfolding—faster, with each passing day. Just live in that idea more and more, and watch it unfold before you, like magic, like a miracle, as it was always supposed to.

☼

Effulgence.

☼

Let your life be about the brilliant radiance that is
housed in your body temple, developed in your mind
and spirit, and was created to shine out to the heavens.
The fiber of our being is stardust. The size of our hearts
is infinite.

# CHAPTER 11

We are all so much more special than we know. And we are all so much less special than we think.

☼

All right, yes, I'll explain that one. Our mind likes to think—thinkthinkthinkthinkthink—all the time, and the thoughts can soar to the heights of ecstasy and plummet to the depths of despondency within a fraction of a second. We think about events that happened long ago and events that are supposed to happen far into the future. Yet none of our thoughts may be real. Our memory of events could be based on misinterpretations and misunderstandings while our fortunetelling talents often leave much to be desired.

The only reality is Truth, what we come to know—right now, this very moment. Truth is God/Goddess/ All That Is. Truth never changes. Truth does not surge to the pinnacles one second and then crash into a canyon a moment later. Truth is an all-powerful, all-loving, all-giving, ever-expanding constant.

We're coming to know ourselves more and more. But there's always more to know, more to open, more to become one with Truth.

And the Truth is we are that Truth...living, breathing, walking, talking emissaries of Truth. We are all magnificent manifestations of the One. But the small self that we *think* is so important—the routines that have to be followed, the goals that have to be met, the problems that have to be figured out—are not important at all. What we come to know about ourselves is what is important.

If nothing else happened other than we realized our full value, that would be enough. And then everything would happen. All the things would be added unto us: peace, prosperity, unity, right livelihood, right relations, right everything.

That's what Yeshua devoted his life to teaching.

It just may have taken quite a while for the lesson to be learned...but perhaps humanity is finally starting to learn.

And for that, all that happened and all that we went through was worth it.

☼

I don't want to reenact all the gruesome details...I just want to tell you a few of the events as they really were, not as one book reported the way they were. Quite a difference. As you know, no one who wrote the gospels was there at the time.

I was.

☼

Let's start with Judas.

Oh, Judas, Judas. My beloved soul brother. One of Yeshua's most beloved friends. He was assigned one of the most important but difficult tasks ever, and was relegated to a status below, some would argue, even mine—that of a traitor. But he had to do what he did, otherwise how else could it have unfolded as it was meant to?

As I mentioned earlier, Judas had a special innocence about him and was more open to learn, change, and transform than were his brethren. He was a gentle lamb of a man, softer even than Yeshua, who had to have more lion in him in order to face such enormous crowds and lay his hands on so many people and do all that he came to do. Judas was at first a very reluctant participant in the necessary events, but as he came to understand the importance of his role he became more willing.

The Sanhedrin, the High Priests, felt threatened by Yeshua. After all, he was single-handedly undoing all their hard work! He persuaded his followers to find their own path.

"Do not take my word as the only word," he would say time and again. "But live by the words that make sense in your own being, as long as they are for the good of all and the harm of none."

The Sanhedrin would find themselves out of a job if Yeshua's students truly followed their own path. Yeshua also spent his days calling to the inner Self, reminding people of their inner authority, just when the priests thought they had them all thoroughly convinced that there was only one outer authority and they were the only intermediaries to that authority.

Speaking of intermediaries....How ironic is it that the followers of the teachings of the one who insisted there is no need for an intermediary between humanity and God, or a savior for humanity, turned him in to an intermediary and/or a savior?! Hmmmmmmm, it is so interesting what we do, is it not? You do not need an intermediary between you and the Divine, he told us time and again. You do not need a savior. You have been saved since the beginning of time. You are the Divine. Did he not say it is written, you are Gods? You! It is not the domain of just the person behind you, nor just the person down the road. You! And it is them, too, of course. It is all of us—the person behind you, the person down the road, the Sanhedrin, the saints, the scribes, the people who devote their lives to God, the modern-day terrorists, the newborns—everyone. But so few know it, so the many unimaginable, unthinkable, inconceivable events are imagined, thought of, conceived of...and continue.

Anyway, back to then: the priests felt threatened, yet they had no law to quash him...so they enlisted the help of Rome. The Twelve were repeatedly approached by various soldiers and even ordinary citizens who wanted to caution them that Yeshua's life was in danger, and possibly theirs as well, but they ignored the warnings. Yeshua knew what was happening, had known his whole life, and was prepared to do whatever it took to leave the biggest message.

He just needed a helper to let it all unfold as it was supposed to. Judas had a very sacred task.

☼

Our last meal together was a holy, holy event with Yeshua and me, the Twelve, Mother Mary, wives and other family members of the apostles, and other friends. We were celebrating Passover, although none of us truly believed the story that the celebration was based on—Angels do not come to kill children in the name of anyone or anything, for any reason, and therefore do not need to pass over certain houses. But oftentimes celebrations take on a greater meaning than the event they are meant to honor, especially if the initial event was a myth, and it was for this greater meaning that we were gathered together.

Judas left the meal early, after a small conference with Yeshua, to do the things you already know about. Yeshua's accusation of betrayal was added to the gospels as filler as the story was told and retold over and over again; he never accused Judas of betraying him. As Judas left, Yeshua looked at me and smiled.

Yeshua, Mary, and I took turns being calm for each other. When his hands and voice were shaking, his mother and I sent him grounding energy and love. When my heart was racing with fear, they would do the same for me. Mary almost fainted at one point, and we sent our loving energy to her.

The Twelve were not apprised of everything that was to unfold until the time that Yeshua felt would be right, so they were happily oblivious to our heart palpitations and tremors. The food and wine flowed and flowed... that is, until Yeshua referred to the food as his body and the wine as his blood.

"I'm going to have to leave you," he told the group of faces that slowly turned ashen as his message struck them. "But you'll be well. Please just take what I've taught you and continue to teach it. That's all I ask of you. Do it in memory of me."

He looked at the eyes that were still staring at him in stunned silence and reiterated his example. "Please, drink of this cup. Please, eat from this plate. Please, take what I've taught you as food for the body and soul and take it onward, beyond the walls of this room, beyond the walls of this city, as far as you can take it."

Several of the Twelve looked at me to see how I was reacting to his words and then looked at his mother. I smiled at them, as reassuringly as I could, as did Mary. Tears were wiped away; urgent questions started but were quieted. The revelry of the night was quickly forgotten and the food and wine remained on the table, untouched after he spoke these words.

We left the room and headed to Gethsemane.

☼

If the disciples kept falling asleep, who was there to hear Yeshua's prayers?

Well, I was.

☼

My beloved did have a moment of reckoning with God and even I was not privy to that. He went amongst the olive trees by himself for a short while but then he returned to me. So most of his time in the garden that night was with me. And most of it was quiet, although much was said.

We looked into each other's eyes. I could see fear cross over his face, followed with resolve; then another moment of trepidation came, followed by yet another decision of faith and trust in the enormous process that was unfolding. I tried to put my own emotions on hold, for now, and to be solely a source of loving support for him. I focused on my heart and breathed in love, breathed out love, breathed in strength, breathed out strength...as I continued to look into his eyes.

About an hour later he looked up at the Heavens and started to pray.

"Abba, Beloved Mother Father God, thou art All That Is. Thou art All That Is. Before the beginning and after the end, is now, always was, and ever shall be." His voice cracked and he looked at me.

"God/Goddess/All That Is," I prayed, "you have created this life, you have created this world, you have created these two people who now speak in your names. You are Life, Life without end, Life everlasting. You are the power that animates everything, everywhere, in the Whole of Creation. You are the love that connects everything, everywhere, in All of Creation." I stopped and opened my eyes to see if he was able to continue again, and he nodded to indicate that he was.

"Beloved, Abba, creator of All That Is, you have

created Life to be an expression of Love, an expression of you. For you so love Creation that you allow it to expand and unfold and express more of you. More love, more joy, more beauty, more peace, more bounty, more… everything." He stopped again and I continued.

"As you are the infinite, eternal expression of Love through and as everything in All of Creation, you are this man and this woman sitting before you. All that we are is comprised of you. Like a drop of water is one with the mighty waters, like one part of the body is one with the whole body, we are one with you. We are you, here to further fulfill your purpose of expressing more of yourself, through and as us—this humble man, this humble woman, your humble servants."

"Beloved," Yeshua whispered. "Beloved. Oh, beloved Life, my beloved Abba." Tears streamed down his face.

"Beloved," I whispered, tears streaming down my face as well, "there is an even greater purpose sometimes that we, your humble servants cannot perceive. We so graciously accept your will to be done here on Earth, here in the physical world and here in our hearts." I swallowed a sob that wanted to rise. "Let us be valiant and accept a greater good." My words transmitted strength to my beloved.

"If in the divine scope of creation, the greatest good is that I am suffered to the cross, then so be it." Yeshua took a deep breath and continued. "I accept that I will do so with grace and dignity, in a manner suited to a son of Creation who knows who he is. Let my love be known, let my words of love reach farther than they would otherwise, let the message of your love be received."

"If it is the divine will for the betterment of all," I prayed, "let us all meet this suffering with courage. Let us, every step of the way, remember who we are, who we are representing, and what we are doing this for. For we know that you so love the world that you would not allow a great suffering for your purpose to be unredeemed for all of your children."

Yeshua's tears stopped. "Beloved, I accept your power as my power. The power that you are is the power that lives in me. The love that you are is the love that lives in me. And so I accept your love to come through me. My breath is you breathing through me, my words are you speaking through me. I am your emissary, as we all are, and I am aware. I do not simply resign myself to a fate I do not desire. I accept the cup that you hand to me. For the good of all." He looked at me for a long moment.

"Beloved Mother Father God," I prayed, "thank you for this life. Thank you for this moment. Thank you for all that will unfold to glorify you. Thank you for the strength that fills us. Thank you for the love that flows through us and into the world, lighting up every person to your Truth."

I stopped talking and looked at him. He took his fingers and ever so gently ran them over my face, tracing my cheekbones and the outline of my features. An angel's touch.

We held each other tightly until Judas arrived with the soldiers.

☼

I know the bible says that Yeshua met with his disciples in that garden frequently, but it was not all that often. So how in creation would Judas have known where we were going to be after seder that night if Yeshua had not told him beforehand?

☼

Judas kissed Yeshua on the cheek and then quickly vanished. The soldiers grabbed hold of my beloved, while he still had a hold of me.

As they seized him by the shoulders and pulled him from me, the others awoke and started to argue with the soldiers. A look from Yeshua quickly silenced them and they retreated to the shadows. Yeshua looked back at me and reached his hands toward mine. The soldiers turned him around and disappeared with him into the night.

My hands were still outstretched to him.

When something horrendous happens to us, we are often wrapped in a cocoon of love by the beings that surround us until we can better handle the pain. When someone dies we are gifted the buffer of numbness until we can handle the loss in doses of healing. Oftentimes we hear of someone encountering a great tragedy and think, "How could they possibly bear it?" Well, they have help. We all have help. And then well past the tragedy itself, many times someone will say to him- or herself, "How can this be? I've grieved already. Here it is back again." Yes, it is back again at a deeper level, going deeper and deeper until the loss is fully accepted and our lives have acclimated to it.

And then sometimes we have both.

As the group left the garden, I was enveloped in the cocoon, but I had glimpses of a black, bottomless abyss of pain, terror, grief, and loss. In the moments of the cocoon, I sent love to Yeshua. In the moments of my abyss, I could feel his love being sent back to me.

☼

I know the chronicles state that Judas killed himself, but I never knew what actually happened to him, at least not while I was still alive. I thought of him often. My deepest wish for him was that he found peace with what he had done and went on to a distant land and lived by what Yeshua had taught him. Given how he'd hung on Yeshua's words and worked diligently to incorporate them into his thoughts and words and moment-by-moment activities, I was certain that he gained the peace that passes human understanding during his life on Earth.

Many, many religions that were formed on what people thought they understood of the Christ say that Jesus was born and died to save humanity. Without Judas, would humanity have been saved?

Was it saved?

☼

It could be. Oh, if we could truly take his words and teachings to heart and lived by them, it could be.

Yes, even in the twinkling of an eye.

☼

If I were to come back today, I would choose to come back as either an Israeli or a Palestinian woman. I would become best friends with an Israeli or a Palestinian woman—whichever one I was not—a soul sister who could make this pre-incarnation agreement with me—and I would sit in the streets in the midst of fighting and break bread with her. If we were killed, we would come back again as exactly the same thing and do the same thing all over again. And if we were killed again, we would come back again, as the same kinds of people again, and do the same thing all over again...

and again...and again...until the time that we could break bread together in the celebration of life and stay alive. And, oh, how we would celebrate!

☼

Peter did deny that he knew Yeshua, three times, that very night. But through the severe self-flagellation that came from betraying his best friend and teacher also came tremendous transformation and resolve. So nothing is ever for naught; it is always for something better. But perhaps next time we will be able to perform the better feat in the first place, and with the outstanding results.

☼

Beloved (I am talking to you now), please do not accept the unfolding of my and Yeshua's life as a sign that you should suffer in any way. This was an exceptional time, with an exceptional chore to undertake. As I have told you, life on the planet was very dense then. Naturally Yeshua could have disappeared into the black of night and left the country if he wanted to. He could have answered Pilate and Herod more fully, even told them the things he knew they wanted to hear, if he wanted to. Many different things could have happened. But it happened the way it was supposed to for a great number of reasons.

It has already been done. There is no need for a repeat.

Your life is to be a celebration of love and joy. Of course everyone suffers to some extent, but please do not take on the mantle of suffering to appease, assuage, placate anyone or anything, least of all for yourself.

And certainly not in God's name...which is your

name, too.

# CHAPTER 12

There is no such thing as death. But the pain felt by those left behind is real. Some will tell you nothing is real, it is all illusion, but that is an illusion. Life is real, Earth is real. To the extent that everything is what you decide it is in your mind, then things are illusory, yes. We are here to feel, experience, live life fully. To thrust our hands into the dirt to plant food that feeds our body and flowers that feed our soul. To dance on stars and rainbows in our daydreams. The pain of childbirth subsides and is forgotten in the thrill of cradling a new life. A love lost subsides in the heart-trembling moments of a new love, starting with loving ourselves in a deeper way. Death is just a gateway to a new life. As we are saying goodbye in this world, our loved one is being welcomed into the new world, just as we were welcomed (or as we should have been) into this world.

There is a fine line...everything is perfect, nothing is a failure, nothing is wrong, and yet most everything can be bettered.

The law of fate is in effect only when our full identity is not known to ourselves. Once we know who we are, along with our purpose, as well as our destiny, then fate cannot govern our lives. There is a timing of things, but there are so many changes of perception, changes of action, chance encounters that can change the direction of a person's destiny.

So, all that happened, happened because it was supposed to. No one was at fault. Yet everyone could have done better, and they did do better in their next incarnations, their next evolutions.

☼

Yeshua often spoke in parables. He also used many metaphors. If the powers that had been could have understood his metaphors and realized the higher truth behind them, things might have been very different. But they were the way they were meant to be. Unfortunately, when Yeshua said that he was here to establish a new domain, which was construed to mean Kingdom, he was misinterpreted and thus viewed to be a threat to both Caesar and the Jewish tradition.

Pilate was a governor from Rome, but he was also a High Priest. He was actually a wonderful man: devoted to his family, fair in his governing, committed to righteousness. He was noted in history as being violent, but it was not so; his underlings thought he was too lenient and performed many senseless torturings and killings in his name, thus thrusting that reputation upon him. Also, the chronicles of time do not care about these kinds of traits, like fairness and devotion, just like the current newspapers might have one column devoted to the wonderful side of humanity and hundreds of other columns devoted to the aberrant, theatrical, crazy machinations of a confused few. So Pilate might have been completely forgotten if he had not had the misfortune of having to decide the fate of someone who became the most important man in history.

People in that time were so scared. Most were completely without a hint of the Truth. Even those who had glimpses of the Truth at times retreated back into themselves. It was too much for them to take in, to handle. Many had been taught by Yeshua but could not incorporate the teachings into their way of living. There is a high amount of responsibility that comes with knowing the Truth.

Pilate had had his glimpses of the Truth and so he did know better. But he was ruling at the time of an angry clashing of these higher truths and the density of fear on Earth. And Yeshua did not help him much either.

*"Art thou a king then?"* Pilate inquired, as you have already heard.

"It was for this purpose that I was born," Yeshua responded. You heard it as, *"Thou sayest that I am a king."*

"What do you mean by those words?"

"My domain is not of this world."

"I'm asking you if you are a king. Answer me."

"I am a king as we all are a king, a queen. I am here to learn and teach Truth, as we all are."

*"What is truth?"*

☼

What a great question!

Yeshua could have answered that Truth is the law that does not change. Truth is an everlasting constant, such as Love. Truth is—well, he could have said anything and Pilate might have let him go, for he was just looking for an answer, any answer.

But Yeshua said none of these things because it was not his destiny for Pilate to release him.

☼

Sequestered in the temple, Mary and I heard the buzz: Pilate could not make the decision and sent him to King Herod. King Herod could not make the decision and sent him back to Pilate. Pilate spoke to the crowd, which was growing by the hour with increasing fervor.

I did not have to hear any of the words to know that he was being lashed. Thirty-nine times. Thirty-nine times! Who could withstand that? I knew his training from the East had helped him here, too. I felt the cords strike his body and concentrated on his heart, transmitting what little strength I had left in that particular moment.

I knew I could not be of service to him if my own energy had dissipated, so I went to the palace gardens and lay on the Earth. I inhaled the scent of the flowers, soaked in the morning sunshine, pulled in the power of the Earth. When I felt a little better I returned to the main temple hall where messengers would return every quarter hour or so with an update. Mary looked as though her spirit had left her body, and I took her out to the gardens as well.

"Mary," she whispered to me, as we lay ourselves down on the ground, "Oh, Mary. I've known this time was coming for his entire life. Perhaps even my entire life. And yet that does not make it any easier."

"No, my beloved mother, it does not. I understand. I, too, have known it was coming since I met him. I've had opportunities to persuade him to change the way things were to go, and yet I did not. You know how he is."

She appeared to garner some strength from my words and she nodded. Yes, she knew how he was. She also knew that her beloved son had had a choice, many times, along the way to this moment. He could have taken another turn in the road at many points, and yet he did not.

I heard in my mind and we heard from the messengers about Pilate asking him if he was a king. For a moment I reminisced about our many discussions and teachings to my students and his on this topic: We are all royalty. We are all divine. We are all children of Eternity.

Yeshua was just a person...a person who happened to be awake, aware. Pilate was just a person...a person who happened to be awake, aware—sometimes. If Pilate had not had a raging, bloodthirsty crowd screaming outside his palace, he might have been a little more perceptive and open to the nuances Yeshua was referring to. But he had Rome weighing down on him, as well as a crowd that was growing vastly more hysterical by the minute.

"Would you crucify your king?" he asked the crowd.

It is written that he was told they had no king but Caesar. That is not correct. They did not specify a king. And if they had, they certainly would not have specified Caesar as their king. Probably a few people called out Caesar's name, perhaps to align with the aggressor, perhaps to promulgate more fear—fear in Pilate that this colony was going to rebel, fear in the soldiers, fear in the crowd that the soldiers were going to turn on them. Perhaps the Roman soldiers were the ones who called out Caesar's name.

It was also said that it was the Jews who crucified him. That was not true either. It was the time, the place, all the people in that particular time and place, the circumstances, the atmosphere. Many people, events, things crucified him, but the Jews were not to blame.

In the season of Passover, to show the spirit of goodwill, the Roman governor would release a prisoner. In an unfortunate twist of irony (or fortunate turn of events, depending on the height of your view), there was another man in prison named Yeshua, who was called the Son of Man. Pilate offered to release him or my Yeshua, the King of the Jews. Perhaps the crowd was confused and did not realize who Pilate meant when he referred to either Yeshua. Even the multitude of Yeshua's students in the crowd might have been confused about which one was which, for Yeshua certainly never assigned a title to himself.

And perhaps something else took over. The crowd itself cannot be faulted for being unaware. Very, very few people come in with this truth, even in the present day; most have to be taught. And if they are not taught by another person, a tragic life experience or close brush with death might teach them. And the worse thing, anywhere, is that a crowd tends to resonate with the lowest common denominator: fear.

Also, in that time, human life was not revered...so condemning someone to death was nowhere near as grave a matter as it is these days—at least in more and more places...civilized places. (And perhaps even the world's largest so-called superpower, which can be civilized when it chooses to remember to be, will learn to revere life—human and animal as well as planetary—as it should be. But that, too, would be another book!) People did not realize their own value, despite how much Yeshua, myself, and others trained in the mysteries tried to impart this information. So when people do not recognize their own intrinsic value, they certainly do not recognize the intrinsic value of another, and unspeakable things can happen as a result...as witnessed day after day after day back then and still today, in the twenty-first century media.

And the crowd Pilate was facing, agitated into a frenzy by the priests with their threats of eternal damnation as a result of disobeying the religious laws, was unstoppable, insatiable. Exasperated, confused, bewildered, and at his wits end, Pilate washed his hands of the whole affair.

☼

Perhaps if he had understood better, he would have

let Yeshua go. And just think how different things would have been for the last two thousand years. Two major world religions embraced by about half the planet would not be here. While so many feel they have been saved by Yeshua, so many died in his name...and what would those people have left behind had they had the chance to live and give their gift?

Even back then we prayed that, after all his teachings about the eternality of life, his crucifixion would be a symbol of life everlasting.

As it was meant to be.

☼

But the results over the subsequent years were supposed to be different. And while nothing is ever a failure, ever, there are better ways to be.

☼

Let's start that better way of being.

☼

Now.

☼

The buzz in the street grew again and the word came to us. The beating had not been enough...he was sentenced to the cross.

Mary and I could barely move. In this, the most overwhelming moment of our lives, we found ourselves kneeling in prayer, allowing ourselves to be filled as we knew that we would have to impart this to our beloved. For a moment we prostrated ourselves on the Earth once again, to draw strength from her, to pass on to him. Then we raced to Pilate's temple, but the throng of people had started to move to the place of the crucifixion—the place of skulls, as it was called. We stumbled through the crowd, nearly tripping over a great number of feet.

I almost doubled over when I saw him—open sores from the whippings, bruised and beaten, blood pouring from the crown of thorns someone had smashed onto his head. I wanted to scream, beat someone myself. But then he looked at me, and I could see that they had not beaten his love or his spirit.

The distance from Pilate's temple to Golgotha was not very far, but that day it seemed interminable. We walked just behind him. The screams and jeers came to me on waves. Sometimes they sounded very far away, as if they were in a thick bubble. But then the bubble would burst and the cacophony would assault me in waves again.

Oh, my beloved; I pray you never know pain like this. But if you should encounter such a tragedy in your life, may you know that it brings you closer to your true nature, closer to yourself, closer to God. All the world's widows and widowers and orphans and soldiers who come home from war with broken bodies and broken spirits...may you know the peace that passes human understanding. May you know that your soul has put you on the high road to Godness. May you know that all the beings of the universe support you, love you, want you to be all that you really are and are there with you in these times.

If I could have traded places with him, I would have. But there was another being who was going to need my attention in about six months, and for a moment here and there I let myself dwell on the joy and wonder of her little body inside mine. And I would pass that feeling on to him; I could tell when it reached him because his shoulders became more erect and his movements seemed a little stronger in those moments.

I watched as he stumbled and fell—once, twice.

A woman wiped his face with a cloth and then handed the cloth to Mary. A man gave him some water.

He fell again.

I watched a woman scream at him and kick dust in his face. For a moment I was captivated by her. Why was she so very angry? What did this have to do with her? Did she even know what she was saying? Did she have any idea what this beautiful man stood for? How would she be if it was her husband who was carrying the instrument of his execution up this hill, in front of such a hate-filled, bloodthirsty mob? Her strange rage fascinated me, almost as if I was watching a being from a far-away planet and was trying to figure out what could possibly be motivating her to act this way. My utter absorption in her antics was a temporary respite from the sheer horror of the moment, but I brought my attention back to Yeshua.

It is all one unified field, I told myself, it is all a thought. Just take from the field, the thought and decide what you want. I took the good I could find in the field and passed it to him with my thoughts. He stood up and continued walking. The blood poured from the wounds on his head.

I stayed close behind him, trying not to dwell on the pain that seared my heart again, but instead focused on sending him love and light. When my work dimmed, he stumbled. When my work was strong, he bore the load far better. The dust clogged my throat and choked me.

We reached the top of the hill where the cross would stand. His clothes were ripped from him as he was shoved down and spread over the cross. I barely heard the pounding of the metal through his flesh as I transmitted love, light, power, healing from the field. The cross was raised up.

A centurion nailed a sign over his head: King of the Jews. The crowd laughed and continued its jeers. Mary and I knelt at the foot of the cross. I did not want to look up at him but I heard his silent request. The brown pools of love met mine. I knew his education in the eastern lands had taught him to put himself out of his body, away from the reach of the pain. But he was beyond exhaustion and needed my strength. I touched the ground and gathered sustenance from the Earth and I passed as much as I could to him.

Over the millennia there have been so many women who have had to watch their husbands die—whether by the noose of a mob, a soldier's bayonet or rifle, the swinging of a ball of spikes by a horseman in an invading group of barbarians, a bomb. Oh, but we have invented so many ridiculously unmentionable, vile, atrocious ways to torture each other. I could not know the pain of each of my sisters, but I felt like I was carrying the pain for them as well as for myself as I had to watch my husband die.

But we are not given anything we cannot handle—much as we would protest otherwise. We are so much stronger than we think we are. We are so much more than we think we are.

"Let them be forgiven," he said to no one in particular. "They know not what they do."

The jeers grew at his words.

"Where is my mother?" he called.

Mary looked up at him and he looked down in her direction. He gave her a look that said, "I love you so. Thank you for all that you have done for me."

She nodded and, as she refused to allow herself to burst into tears, she bowed her head in prayer.

"I am thirsty," he called out.

Someone, I do not know who, held a saturated rag up to him. It seemed to revive him, for a moment. He gathered his strength to speak and a hush fell over the crowd. He looked at me.

"Mary," he whispered.

"Yeshua," I whispered back. The look we exchanged surely must have conveyed the greatest love a man and woman could have ever shared.

"For this purpose I was born." He bowed his head. The drone of the crowd grew deafening.

No, he could not be dead yet, I assured my screaming heart. It takes days to die from this form of murder. On the other hand, my heart lifted slightly at the thought that his ordeal was over. The bubble surrounded me again and the screams of the crowd seemed very far away.

A centurion thrust a spear in his side. Blood flowed but there was no reaction, no sign of life.

He was taken from the cross. Despite the warnings from the guards, I draped myself over his body for a moment and then ran my hands over his still-warm face and chest. A guard pulled me from him. Several centurions took his body, followed by several more who were assigned to ensure that his body was taken to the graveyard and nowhere else. Joseph followed them to request the body from Pilate.

I was not allowed to go with them. I sank to the ground and found myself staring at the cross, barely even seeing the blood that still glistened in the light of the day, which was turning darker by the moment by approaching storm clouds. I felt a familiar hand take mine, the loving hand of my husband's brokenhearted mother, and I kissed it. I know not how long we remained there. I could still smell his scent in the air and could still hear his voice despite the initial booms of thunder.

At some point Mary and I found ourselves taken by a donkey cart to the temple, where we collapsed.

☼

I never understood why the writers of the gospels altered his last words, spoken from the cross, so very drastically. If they were trying to elevate him to the status of God, the beseeching that they attributed to him was very unGodlike, whereas what he said in reality was very divine.

Even a misunderstanding of the nuances of the language could not explain or excuse such a drastic shift...but as we know, it was done here and at least a thousand other times.

☼

Oh, Life.
And it was for this purpose he was born.

# CHAPTER 13

"Mary! Mary!" A hand shook me roughly. "You must come."

I did not want to go anywhere. I wanted to stay in the soft, warm arms of sleep, where the pain had subsided, where I could float to the other worlds and forget everything that had happened here in this world that day.

"Mary! You're needed!" I perceived this to be the voice of Satan, if there was such a thing as Satan, which of course there is not, because it was stealing me away from the sweet numbness brought by sleep.

"She's not moving!" The interloping Satan was apparently joined by one of his satanic helpers. Yes, this might have been an extreme reaction to two people who were just trying to wake me up, but I had been through an extreme event.

"Well, small wonder, with what she's been through. Have someone carry her. She'll wake up along the way."

I felt myself lifted up and carried outside to a donkey cart. I was vaguely aware that I was being taken across the city to the gravesite. The centurions were not there; I was informed later that they had been drugged and dragged to the hills outside of Jerusalem. And the two interlopers that I had dubbed as straight from the gates of Hell quickly shifted to messengers from Heaven.

The scent of the herbs brought me to full alertness instantly. I recognized one of the figures leaning over the body.

"Joseph, what are you doing?"

"Mary, thank God you are here. Get to work, my

dear."

I watched Joseph press a poultice to the body. A glimmer, a quickening of hope started in the recesses of my heart, before my mind could even begin to grasp the enormity of what lay before me.

Why would he be doing that, unless......unless......

I took the hand of my beloved. It was not very warm, but it was not cold either, and it had been hours since they took him from the cross. The part of me that was fully aware of the magnitude of this moment before my mind caught up instructed me to hold his hand to my heart to transmit energy. Finally my mind let it in.

Oh, Yeshua! My beloved! You are still with me, on this side of the veil!

"Why did not you tell me?" I hissed at Joseph.

"We thought it best, given your condition. In case he did not make it. I did not want to give you false hope."

"My condition? Good Goddess above! I'm bringing in life, not leaving it. Have you taken leave of your mind? I know more about healing than the rest of you put together. Move aside!"

☼

I sat with him that night, the whole next day, and late into the next night, applying herbs, transmitting love and light, gently talking to him. Even my long experience as a healer could not tell me if he was more alive than dead, or more dead than alive at times. I had seen him many times in deep, deep samadhi—where his mind was away in the mental realm while his lungs were barely taking oxygen, his heart barely beating. I cupped my hand an inch from his face and felt a cool rush, not the usual heat that passes between two human beings.

The herbs were changed. I held his hand, softly

stroking his palm with my fingers, to assure him that I was there.

"I love you," I whispered. "I love you." I bent my head down, my hands in prayer position, pressed to my forehead.

"I love you, too," I heard. I looked up but his face was still, his lips had not moved. He had definitely spoken to me, but from which realm I was not certain. Was it the realm beyond this life, or was he still here? I bent my head down again, leaning on one arm and wrapping the other arm around his waist.

☼

Joseph gently picked me up off his body. I did not know how long I had been asleep. "My dear Mary, you must leave now, you must rest. And not just for your sake. I will watch him. You just go get some sleep now."

I let myself be led out of the tomb and then I slipped to the ground.

How I got from the tomb to my home I had no idea. I had a vague sense of being relieved of my clothing and helped into my bed. And then there was just the quiet of deep, dreamless sleep.

☼

The first rays of light touched my face. I had a moment of bliss as my body prepared to meet another day; but then my heart skipped a beat, ringing a warning bell, remembering it all before my mind caught up—there was something...not quite...right. What—?

The trauma and elation of the previous two days flooded my entire being. In one swift movement I was out of bed, into my garments, and out the door. I raced across the city. Few people were up this early in the morning.

I arrived at the tomb but the stone had been rolled back. There was only a pile of clothing on the flat rock in the antechamber. Somebody had taken him!

My hand clutched my heart, trying to lessen the palpitations. I tried to catch my breath as well as to catch a coherent thought. Off in the distance I saw a hooded figure and ran towards it, barely able to see anything through my tears.

"Where is he?" I blurted out when I reached the man. "What have you done with him? Please tell me!"

The man turned to me, his hood covering much of his face. But the sides of his mouth slowly turned upward...into a slightly crooked smile. I fell into his arms.

"My Mary, my darling," he whispered. *"Why seek ye the living among the dead?"*

☼

So, yes, there was a resurrection.

☼

I understand you might have heard the story a little differently. But consider this...it takes days to suffocate on a cross. Yes, Yeshua lost a lot of blood and was beaten terribly and was nailed to the cross, when often people were just tied. But when someone dies on the cross, it is because they suffocate...they cannot talk.

Joseph had procured over a hundred pounds of herbs. He would not have done that if he was preparing a body for burial. He would have done that if he was trying to bring someone back from the doorway to the other side, however.

How often over the centuries, do you think, has a

condemned person been given something to drink? They've just nailed him to a cross—he's bleeding, exposed to the vultures to come pluck out his eyes. Why would they suddenly care enough to give him something to drink? But the liquid on the cloth had contained an opiate, to knock him out and put him out of his pain to conserve some strength. And it did not come from the soldiers.

I was angry with Joseph for not telling me the plan, but he insisted he thought he was helping the whole situation.

"If I had known, I would have been able to send more healing energy through his suffering," I said, "instead of trying to help him cross to the other side."

"But he had to look dead, my dear, to the soldiers. What you ended up doing was perfect. The Romans were completely convinced he was dead, and yet he lives, in secret."

"Where do they think the body went?"

"Hopefully they think someone stole it, to claim a miraculous resurrection straight to Heaven or some such tale."

Yeshua was still so weak from the ordeal, but his eyes remained those mystical spheres. I gazed at the blazing orbs of light that were his eyes for hours at a time, so happy to be seeing them again.

We were hidden away in the caves in the hills beyond the city. Mary was told of his survival on that Sunday after the crucifixion and was brought to him. No one outside of his mother, Joseph, and a couple of others knew, but Joseph had appointed several men to stand guard at all hours. They were well-paid for their service and their silence.

As he recovered and regained his strength, Yeshua wanted to see his disciples. We heard that Judas had left, condemned by the others, who did not understand the whole process. Of course they would not understand—they still thought Yeshua was dead and Judas had betrayed him.

Joseph tried to dissuade Yeshua from his plans, and especially me from accompanying him. "They will be looking for you," he said to me. "They will be on the lookout for you, everywhere."

But Yeshua was not to be discouraged. "The point of living on is to live, to move on. At least for those who would understand."

"But you chose a crucifixion for a purpose," Joseph said. "You could have convinced Pilate otherwise. So you must have wanted to suffer such a horrible death for some higher reason."

"There is life. And there is Life."

Mary and I stayed together in the caves while he was taken under the cover of night back into the city.

☼

The apostles were holed up in a room in an inn, fearful that the Romans and even some of their countrymen were looking for them, as well. Provisions were brought to them by the young son of the innkeeper, who had no idea who they were

Yeshua was let in through a back door, by the innkeeper, who also had no idea who he was, although how that was possible, no one knew. But he joined his men in the room. They were stunned silent for several moments, as Yeshua relayed to me later.

"But Teacher, you died," Mark finally said. "We saw you taken from the cross."

"*Behold my hands and my feet, that it is I myself; handle me, and see; for a spirit hath not flesh and bones, as ye see me have.*"

☼

Yes, he actually did say "Behold" fairly often...at least the Aramaic version of "Behold."

☼

The whole trial and crucifixion was a travesty of justice, but it served a purpose.

☼

In a way all of us go through a crucifixion, where we die to an old way of being. In Yeshua's case, he wanted the world to die from its old way of thinking. He wanted to dislodge it from its sleepy, murky stuckness where what has gone before will be the way it is always done... where the laws and rules had become more important than the changing situations of human beings.

And perhaps the world did die to its old way of thinking...a little. We misjudged the extreme density of life on Earth and how long things can take, though. In other planes a thought can manifest instantly. On Earth, sometimes, it can take a couple thousand years. Or more.

We were dealing with people who dealt only with the physical. Their hands worked the soil, or worked wood, or other firm, solid things of the Earth—a counterbalance to the very unfirm, unsolid mysteries of life and the mind and spirit. They were so very simple. They had simple rules but little room for forgiveness of transgressions. They did things the way they always had, the way their ancestors had done before them, and they assumed their children and children's children would do things the same way. They lived in the creature part of the human brain.

They followed the laws of our time, both Rome's laws and the religious laws. Both were developed to make a precise practice of life. But we taught things differently. We taught of a greater Life, a greater Love, that we all possess and can access at any time, instantly. There is no reward awaiting us after this Life. We are the Reward. Now.

He, and I, had attained the Christ consciousness. Buddha consciousness. God consciousness. We were awake and aware, enlightened, open to the God/Goddess within, the domain of Heaven that lives within each of us. Christ, the anointed one. And, by the way, remember who anointed him? You would have known even if I had not already told you. But the Christ comes without an anointment or anything from the outside. It lives within all of us and is experienced to the extent that we allow that experience.

"For this purpose I was born." The Bible quotes that as *"My God, my God, why hast thou forsaken me?"* If that one line is so extremely discombobulated, imagine how off the target everything else that was written could be. And then just think of how misguided people have been...and lo the many defilements of his name through acts of horror.

By Yeshua's apparent death he wanted to show the temporary temporality of this life. It worked to some extent. But then his life was misconstrued and his teachings were taken out of context, other crazy ideas were added, and over the next two millennia it seemed like humanity was going backward.

Except when it was not. There have been uplifting periods, as if to remind us all that we are actually moving along, like a baby kicking within the womb lets its mother know that it is moving along, all is well. It is time for this particular baby, Christ consciousness, to be born.

All is well. Truly.

☼

He continued to meet with the apostles as often as he could, without jeopardizing their safety or his own. He met and satisfied the doubts of his beloved doubting Thomas. Finally Joseph urged him to stop returning due to some rumors that were starting on the streets of Jerusalem and he met with them one last time.

☼

"Tell them what I have taught you," he repeated to them. "But please, you do not have to talk about me. Just *love one another; as I have loved you.*"

# CHAPTER 14

It was that magic moment between asleep and awake, when the mind is somewhat aware that it is awake but it is still cavorting in the other spheres, dancing in the dreamworld. I sensed that he was awake, which was affirmed by the kiss on the top of my head.

"My darling, I must go." His voice relayed that he had been crying, so I knew he did not mean just another jaunt to Jerusalem.

A void opened up inside me. I could not see anything, just blackness. My being straddled an infinite chasm. If I slipped into that chasm I would never return. I burrowed further under the bedcovers, as if to shield myself from his words. One parting I could do; another seemed beyond my capacity.

"We cannot hide away in a cave forever. I do not want to leave you. But if they find me and they find you with me......"

All my life I had been prepared for this moment. Days spent in darkness. Nights of terror. Delusions from severe hunger. Thousands of hours of prayer and meditation. Washing feet and anointing the crown of many people, not just my beloved. Years of teaching about the beauty of Life and about God. And since I met him, I knew there would come a day when our time together would come to an end. So I knew, but that did not make the moment any easier. Perhaps I thought that fateful day had been tricked into disappearing forever...which only made this moment all the harder.

We had been in hiding for over two months. My belly was starting to proudly display the new being who was coming.

I opened my eyes and could see that he had not slept.

"I do not want to go. I do not want to go. But we have to be strong. There is a much bigger view here. Knowing that can be our sustenance."

"Where will you go?"

"Back to the east. They seem to have a far greater knowing of some things. I will be safe and I can continue the teachings from there. Someday all people will be able to understand them better—I am certain of that."

I did not say anything.

"You will be safe, too. Joseph can take you west, and north, across the waters. And you can continue the teachings as well."

I nodded. If it were just me, I would go with him, no matter what he said. If I died, well, so be it, I could go on to whatever was next. But it was not just me any more. For a moment I detested the life inside me, but just for a moment...for that life was him, too...a way for him to still be present in this realm, a way of carrying him into the future of this world, as his son was doing already, no matter what other worlds Yeshua would go to.

"When, my darling?"

"The day after tomorrow."

☼

We were often left alone in the cave, while our guardians stayed outside. But on this, our last night, they seemingly vanished completely, although I knew they could not be far because their entire purpose there was for our protection. Mother Mary was going to join him on his journey, meeting up with him in Persia, and she had already left. Saying goodbye to her was harder than saying goodbye to my own mother when she was dying.

My spirit had been coaxed, taught, developed to be primary in my life. But this night belonged to my body. I would be with him in spirit always, but this was the last night I would lie next to him, feeling the length of his body next to mine, hearing his heartbeat, tasting the saltiness of him, feeling the brush of his eyelashes against my cheek. As always when our bodies came together, the world faded away and there was only his entire being pressing against me, only his breath, only his tongue tracing the outline of my neck, my shoulder, my breasts. There was only the feeling of him slowly entering me, filling me for the last time. I watched the fireburst for the last time, and we lay awake almost all night, just holding each other, relishing the physical touch for the last time. And even with this embrace of the physical plane, I heard the music of the spheres with him one last time.

☼

It passed too quickly. Dawn's streak appeared in the east.

"My beautiful queen."

My heart hurt too much to answer, to even look at him.

"Please look at me."

I turned my head towards him. The soft eyes glowed at me, barely disguising his own torment. He kissed me and then slipped out of the bed.

He turned back at the opening of the cave, his eyes betraying his distress. It was now my turn to carry us. I held my belly. "The bigger view," I whispered.

He nodded. And then he was gone.

☼

I had been so strong all my life, but I could not summon that strength now. I returned to my quarters at the temple and lay in bed for hours. Joseph came and spoke of plans. I nodded, although I barely heard what he said. Oils, ointments, herbs, and other provisions were gathered from my urns and storage compartments. My clothes were packed up.

As evening came I stumbled out the front door, wondering how I even had the strength to stand and when I even had dressed myself. I collapsed in the garden by my front door.

"You have to eat, my dear," I heard a vaguely familiar voice tell me. But I could not move. I pushed Rachel's loving arms away from me. She knew enough to leave me alone.

Morning came and found me still slumped in front of my quarters. I stumbled up the path to the roadway and headed toward the hills and the sands.

And this was where you came in so many pages ago.

☼

My hand still pressed against my swelling belly as I joined the others, who had been waiting for me at secret place. We traveled by night to the sea and then, once we arrived at the waters, we waited until night came again.

I thought of my preparations during the travel times, of how much I hated to leave home and tried to heal that, knowing that life might arrange a harder lesson for me at some point. This was the point. But at this point I only wanted to go, far away, and set up a new home for myself and our child.

Joseph had made arrangements for our transport, as he had arranged everything else. I allowed unknown hands in the darkness to lead me to the water's edge, where I heard the waves gently lapping on the shore and against the vessel. I did not know how many others were in the boat, perhaps a dozen, perhaps more. Other than my beloved Rachel, I did not even know who my traveling companions were. I allowed myself to be guided into the boat and then led to the blankets and bedding that had been set out for me. I stretched out as someone pushed us away from the shore, shielded by the darkness of the hour. The sweet oblivion of sleep took me before I even finished pulling the covers over my head.

The boat sailed for Gaul.

☼

"Beloved, I will always be with you...always." He said this to me, and to you.

"Beloved, as will I." I said this to him, and now I say it to you.

☼

Now is the time.

# CLOSING

And so you have it. Not exactly a story about God nor a story about a whore, eh? As you so very well know, in the course of history Yeshua was quickly elevated to that unattainable level and I was quickly relegated to that undesirable level. Either direction, we were unreachable and untouchable. But now that you have the full story, you know we were not God and a whore. We were just like you. The only difference was that we allowed our bodies, hearts, minds, spirits to dance in ecstasy more often than most. We loved more than most. We could see the possibilities more than most. We shared these teachings with others more than most.

Despite my fears earlier that day at the rocks, even though he was still in body yet could not be with me, he never did leave me. And I never left him.

The love Yeshua and I had was truly divine, and there was going to be no repeat of it. I did not search out companionship after our parting, for he was still with me. I raised our child with the help of Rachel and my new family of friends—the people of our new village.

Yeshua stayed with his son for several years on his way back to the East. He was with his beloved mother when she left her body. I had my beloved family around me when I exited this realm, and he had many followers around him when he exited around the same time.

I knew I would be with him forever and I was patient. We met in the ethereal world, euphoric in our reunion...and we still are.

☼

Sometimes the pain can make us bitter, sometimes it can even kill us. But sometimes the pain sears the soul, burning away anything unlike who we truly are, leaving the core of our greatness. The moments of anguish become avenues for ecstasy. The times of trial become a path of awakening.

Right now, this very moment, there are people in so much pain they want to leave their bodies. Right now, this very moment, there are people falling in love. Right now, this very moment, new life is being created. Right now, this very moment, someone is in so much pain he is killing someone else.

To take a hammer and pound a nail through someone's hand, through someone's foot. To leave them on a cross for the birds to peck out their eyes. What could possibly exist in the heart of someone who could do that? The ones who direct these actions are far away from the streets, where the activity takes place. But the actual people who drive a nail through someone's flesh, at someone else's command—what could they be thinking? They do it for the money, they do it because they are simple and do as they are instructed, they do it because they do not know any better. They do it because they do not know who they are. They do not love themselves—far from that: they despise themselves. How else could they inflict pain on another?

The one who would snuff out the breath of another, who apparently has the power in that moment, does not hold the power for long. There are other worlds, other dimensions where the scales of justice are balanced, where retribution is gained. And yet, it may have been an agreement that that life was extinguished, for the growth of both souls and for all those who knew them. Who knew what Pilate, Herod, Judas, and the man who pounded the nails through Yeshua's hands and feet set up to learn in that life? Actually, I know now, and they accomplished their directives.

And really, there are no differences. We are the same. There is no difference between Yeshua and the man who drove the nails through his flesh. There is no difference between Yeshua and me. There is no difference between you and us. We are all one. We are all the same, just different holy facets of the same holy jewel.

Yes, the ground is holy, because you, beloved you, beautiful you, walk on it.

He and I only walked this planet once. It does not matter how many times you have walked the planet because life is eternal, you are eternal, you have been here forever, and you will be here forever. So no one is the reincarnation of us...and everyone is the reincarnation of us...and everyone else who has gone before. Earth is a wonderful training ground for many things, and many have chosen to come back again and again. Others receive their training elsewhere and then come here. It is a matter of soul choice, whatever we deter-mine is best for our soul's evolution.

My beloved Yeshua was no different than anyone, except that he had opened his heart to love more. And in the resulting effulgence, all things were possible to him. He was about love; that is all he was about. And yet more have been and still are belittled, judged, vilified, and murdered in his name than in anyone else's name, ever. How could that possibly be, for a man based entirely on love? How could anyone think that the divine creator of this universe would choose some of its children over others?

And yet, there is still nothing wrong. There are no mistakes. We just get to try it out and then perhaps try it out again, like a message written in the sand, waiting for a wave to wash it away, and allow a new message to be written.

☼

Please take his words and not any subsequent actions attributed to him. "They will know you by how you love one another, not by how you worship me," is what he said again and again. Please love one another. Please do not elevate him to a status you think you cannot attain. He, and I, did not go anywhere you cannot go. Live there now.

Hopefully his true message will land on ears that can hear it, ears that are finally earnestly yearning to hear this message and live a life of joy and ease and magnificence. And perhaps peace will come to our lands at last.

Be humble in your magnificence...otherwise what you have will not be magnificence. One of the hardest things to do is stay humble while we are realizing how incredibly wonderful we are. The ego wants to take all kinds of credit; it is really moving the ego out of the way, however, that allows our magnificence to shine through. It is great to stand tall, aware of our brilliance, but the power is in the humble person, not the one all puffed up with false authority. Open to your power—the kind of power where you fall to your knees in awe and reverence and gratitude for the majesty of it all, for the miracle that is this life.

Where does individuality come into play? If all of this is God, and we are emanations of God, where can we as the individual emanations take any credit? The only place we can have the credit is if we allow ourselves to move out of the way and let God shine through our lives. There, we can take credit for that. We can also take credit for our diligence, perseverance, practicing patience, kindness, doing more than expected—even just one more thing each day, because it often would be so much easier to do things another way. We can take credit for taking the holy hand of the Goddess and allowing her to guide us on our journey, telling us what to do, what to say. We don't have to do anything alone, on our own...because that would be impossible anyway, even though so many try so hard and nearly kill themselves in the process.

But the air we breathe is God's air, is God. The glorious tree, the mighty ocean, all of it, everything, is God's creation, is God. The tree is no less glorious because it did not come here and manifest on its own, of its own accord. The ocean is no less mighty because it is God's ocean. Indeed, it is more. The works that come through us are God's work, and we are no less worthy; indeed, we are more. It is all God, playing and dancing and expressing throughout infinity.

There is a higher knowing that shows itself in every work of art, in every piece created by a master craftsman, in every moment of special care that a mother gives her child, in every teaching that a healer passes on. We have our talents and passions that show us what we are to do on this particular journey on Earth, what our gifts are, what our missions are. And we show up and offer those and allow the higher knowing to take it farther than it would of its own accord. We all have direct access to the divine muse. We are the Divine, so the divine muse resides in us.

How do we know what our gifts are? We simply follow where our greatest love and joy lead us.

The lives of the great masters and avatars can sometimes look messy and ragged. But you know them by the gifts they leave behind—their music, their artwork, their creations, their messages. They can sometimes look like average people, struggling to make a living, to keep a relationship. They have been imprisoned unjustly. They have been hopelessly in debt. They have been homeless. They have been...a great many unpleasant things. But their gifts are in what they left behind...which has often created a world better than it was before.

These days, however, we know more; there is no need to have messy and ragged be a part of your life any longer. There is room for expansion in every dimension, and it can be easy in your relationships, in your purse, in your body temple, in your work, in your world.

And you do not have to be out in the world, a public figure, if that is not your calling. If you can maintain this knowing of divinity in the privacy of your own home, even by yourself, that will raise the planet. If you can transmit this higher place to your family, or even just those you come into contact with during the day, that, too, is a major benefit to the planet as well. The moments of holding your child's hand as she falls asleep, giving your spouse an extra smile as he or she goes to the day's work, smiling at the homeless person on the street—these are the special times that make life on Earth so meaningful and create more miracles than the simple acts themselves would suggest.

Beloved, you have so much to give. Please do not hold it back. It is what you came for. Make love, make art, make babies, make peace, make music, make joy, make poetry. Let it come to you on the rays of starlight. Let it be easy, let it be fun. Live by grace.

Honor the teachings. Honor Yeshua and me, too, but not from a place of being lower than us. Honor all the great teachers. Honor yourself; you are on the same level—you are a great teacher, too. You can walk on water and turn water into wine and become enlightened and lo those many other things, too. You can protect the environment, change the system so that our abundance of food and water get to all the people everywhere, and let justice, freedom, and peace reign. Now! Today!

When we say you are an infinite being, it does not mean that you step into this infinity when you die. You are that infinite being now, right now, with the infinite possibilities in the tip of your finger, your heart, your mind, your soul, and your spirit.

Do not just have hope that things will be all right anymore. Hope can make people passive, even lazy, thinking that someone else will do the work. *Know* that things are unfolding as they should and do your work in yourself, in your sphere, and in the world to make the unfoldments higher and higher. We simply cannot disregard the problems anymore. It is time to wake up.

☼

He said, "For this purpose I was born."

To whom much is given, much will be expected. When I was trained as a priestess and a healer, I knew my life would be about service: I came here to teach, heal, lift up humanity, and be the counterpart of one of the most important men who ever walked the face of the Earth. The moment Yeshua told his parents that he was about his Mother Father God's business, he turned his life to service, and a higher service there has never been. The road was so rocky at times, at times tragic, but there was more joy, love, and beauty than we even imagined, and it was the greatest gift we could give. It was our honor.

But we did nothing that you cannot do—and you can do it without pain and tragedy. And now that you know we were just like you, you can be just like us.

☼

My beloved did *not* want us all to think we could just sail on his wings to some distant Heaven, some far-off reward that happens after we die. That belief can also make us passive and lazy—if we're waiting for the better life to happen later, we don't have to put forth the effort to making the better life here and now. When we are spiritually awake and mature, however, we know that everything is connected, and can take better care of ourselves, each other, and the planet.

If anyone feels threatened by the ideas I put forth here, I invite them to examine why in the world they feel threatened. If they were to put forth their own beliefs when I was on Earth, they would not have threatened my beliefs at all. If they have to feel that they are the chosen people, or the saved people, or extra special in any way, I would invite them to examine why they need to feel that way. Why would the Universe/God/Creator make anything in creation that wasn't special? Why does there need to be a special club? There is a special club—and we're all in it! Let's celebrate!

Yeshua and I wanted us all to acknowledge the God/Goddess within and live fully from our own higher authority. While every religion leads people to God, some very well-meaning but misguided churches have waylaid the process. We can go directly to God! We are God! (Now that line can make some people literally crazy, so remember, we each are not *all* of God, with complete omniscient, omnipresent knowledge of All; but we are each a divine drop of God, and omniscient, omnipresent knowledge resides in us.) We do not need Jesus Christ's help to get there. We are already there! And we are the Christ—each one of us, as soon as we awaken to it.

Now let's celebrate our lives, as well as his, as well as everyone else's. Let's praise our names, as well as his, as well as everyone else's. Let's revel in our son- and daughtership of the Most High, as well as his, as well as everyone else's. Let's glorify God, which is everything, everywhere, including you, including him, and including me...which is *exactly* what he would have wanted.

☼

In the beginning of this story I said that I knew that what we had done was for the evolution of everyone in the past two thousand years and everyone yet to come. That is the power that lives in you, too.

Quite often when a bright light comes into the world, the powers that be want it extinguished. This is what life on Earth sometimes does to people who shine. But we must all shine anyway. Radiate. Full beam. And soon the powers that be will be us all, radiating... spiraling upward in complete, glorious brilliance and rapture.

Come, dance with us.

Welcome to eternal life.

THE END

# KJV BIBLE VERSES

John 10:10

Matthew 23:11

Matthew 15:11

John 5:6

John 5:6

Mark 3:33

John 14:6 (first part)

John 14:6 (second part)

John 1:50

Matthew 8:22

Matthew 6:22 and Luke 11:34

Matthew 18:19

Matthew 6:25

Luke 12:32

Matthew 21:22

Matthew 7:7 and Luke 11:9

John 3:16

Matthew 5:9

Matthew 6:22

Matthew 5:14-16

Matthew 6:11 and Luke 11:3

Matthew 5:44

John 3:3

John 18:37

John 18:37

John 18:38

Luke 24:5

Luke 24:39

Matthew 27:46 and Mark 15:34

John 15:1

IN LOVING MEMORY
OF

*My Mother*

# THANK YOU

Mary and Yeshua

Rev. Dr. Michael Beckwith,
Agape International Center of Truth, Culver City, CA

Rev. Karyl Huntley and Rev. Dr. Lloyd Tupper,
Golden Gate Center for Spiritual Living,
Corte Madera, CA

Grace Sears and Kiara Windrider

The authors Emmet Fox, *The Sermon on the Mount*
(HarperCollins, 1966); Joel Goldsmith, *The Infinite
Way* (DeVorss & Company, 1992); and Holger
Kersten, *Jesus Lived in India* (Penguin, 2001)

Rocco Errico, "Light on the Language of Jesus,"
featured monthly in the *Science of Mind* magazine

Barbara Marx Hubbard

Geoff Benzing

Alicja, Amaeya, Anton, Betsey, Chrisann,
Eileen, Rev. Georgia, Jeanne Marie,
Rev. Lee, Marion, Nancy, Susan

Rev. Katherine Revoir and Linda Donahue

Barbara Cox

My darling children and my beloved husband

# BOOKS BY
# ANN CRAWFORD

Available in paperback, e-book,
and audiobook versions

*Life in the Hollywood Lane*

*Spellweaver*

*Angels on Overtime*

*Mary's Message—*
*The Alternative Story of Mary Magdalene and Jesus*

*Visioning—Creating the Life of Our Dreams*
*and a World that Works for Us All*

Made in United States
Orlando, FL
25 March 2024

45121964R10121